Thomas Jefferson's
Library

Thomas Jefferson. This replica of a bust by Jean Antoine Houdon is exhibited near the entrance to the Main Reading Room in the Great Hall of the Library of Congress.

Thomas Jefferson's Library

A Catalog with the Entries in His Own Order

edited by

James Gilreath
Library of Congress

Douglas L. Wilson
Knox College

LIBRARY OF CONGRESS   WASHINGTON   1989

Library of Congress Cataloging-in-Publication Data

Gilreath, James, 1947–
    Thomas Jefferson's Library.

    1. Jefferson, Thomas, 1743–1826—Library
Catalogs. 2. Bibliography—Early printed books—
Catalogs. 3. Classification—Books. I. Wilson
Douglas L. II. Library of Congress. III. Title.
Z997.J48G55   017′.6   88–607928
ISBN 0–8444–0634–1 (alk. paper)

This book is printed on acid-free paper.

Book and cover design by William Chenoweth.

Covers: Photographic reproductions of a marbled paper used for the endpapers in a number of Thomas Jefferson's books. The marbling effect was achieved by floating colors in a solution and then dipping a sheet of paper into the mixture. This example of marbled paper is from Jefferson's copy of Fortune Barthelemy de Felice's *Code de l'Humanité* (Yverdon, 1778). Photograph by Pamela Spitzmueller.

For sale by the Superintendent of Documents, U.S. Government Printing Office
Washington, DC 20402

CONTENTS

Foreword   vii

Introduction   1

    Selected Reading List   12

    Editorial Note   13

Catalogue

I. Memory
    1. Antient History   17
    2. Modern History. Foreign   21
    3. Modern History. British   27
    4. Modern History. American   31
    5. History—Ecclesiastical   34
    6. Natural Philosophy   35
    7. Agriculture   36
    8. Chemistry   39
    9. Surgery   40
   10. Medicine   40
   11. Animals. Anatomy   44
   12. Animals. Zoology   44
   13. Botany   46
   14. Mineralogy   47
   15. Occupations of Man. Technical Arts   48
II. Philosophy
   16. Ethics   52
          Moral Philosophy   52
          Law of Nature and Nations   56
   17. Religion   58
   18. Jurisprudence. Equity   64
   19. Jurisprudence. Common Law   65
   20. Jurisprudence. Law—Merchant   74
   21. Jurisprudence. Law—Maritime   75

22. Jurisprudence. Law—Ecclesiastical   76
23. Jurisprudence. Foreign Law   77
24. Politics   79
25. Mathematics. Pure. Arithematic   93
26. Mathematics. Pure. Geometry   94
27. Physico-Mathematics. Mechanics, Statics, Dynamics,
    Pneumatics, Phonics, Optics   95
28. Astronomy   96
29. Geography   98

III. Fine Arts
30. Architecture   108
31. Gardening, Painting, Sculpture   109
32. Music   110
33. Poetry. Epic   111
34. Romance. Tales—Fables   113
35. Pastorals, Odes, Elegies   115
36. Didactic   118
37. Tragedy   120
38. Comedy   121
39. Dialogue—Epistolary   122
40. Logic, Rhetoric, Orations   123
41. Criticism. Theory   125
42. Criticism. Bibliography   126
43. Criticism. Languages   127
44. Polygraphical   132

Appendix
Some pages from the printed catalog of 1815   134

FOREWORD

This slim but important volume makes available for the first time in print an illuminating historical document until recently believed to have been lost—namely, Thomas Jefferson's own classification of the sixty-seven hundred books he sold to the federal government after the British had destroyed the congressional library in Washington during the War of 1812. Far from being a mere list of titles, Jefferson's catalog of his "great library" reflects the Virginian's attempt to categorize all knowledge and, as such, it provides unique insight into the world view of this multisided genius. Given the catholic range of Jefferson's informed intellect, the catalog will be of serious interest to students, academic and otherwise, in scores of disciplines.

James Gilreath and Douglas L. Wilson, editors of the catalog, know as much as anyone today about Jefferson's love affair with the printed word. Like all superior researchers, Gilreath and Wilson are superb detectives. Their lengthy and enlightening introduction tells the story of their scholarly sleuthing and suggests the catalog's significance as a rare guide to Jefferson and his times.

As one who professed "I cannot live without books," Jefferson surely must have died a bit with the sale of his premier collection in 1815. Fortunately he was spared knowing of the subsequent disappearance of his classification scheme, which is now reclaimed for posterity over 160 years after his death, thanks to its publication under the appropriate aegis of the Library of Congress.

Daniel P. Jordan

Daniel P. Jordan, Director
*Thomas Jefferson Memorial
Foundation, Inc.*

Jefferson's library at Monticello. The bookcases now in the room bold duplicate examples of volumes once owned by Thomas Jefferson. Their arrangement shows his preference for grouping his books by size on the shelves. Photograph courtesy of the Thomas Jefferson Memorial Foundation, Inc./James Tkatch.

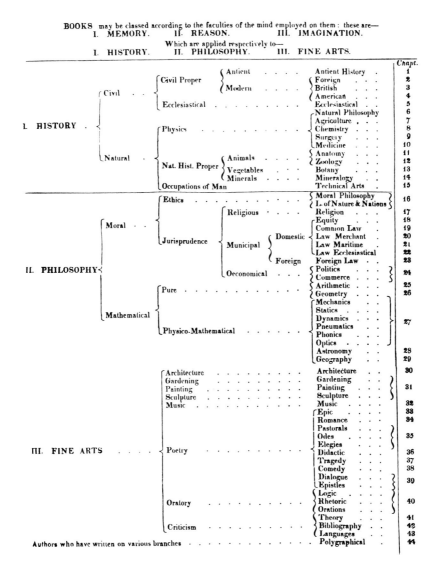

The classification scheme Jefferson devised for his collection as it appears in the Catalogue of the Library of the United States *(Washington: Printed by Jonathan Elliot, 1815). The Library of Congress adopted Jefferson's organization of knowledge, using it to classify its growing collection of books for most of the nineteenth century.*

A selection of Thomas Jefferson's books from the collection he sold to Congress in 1815 after the congressional library in the Capitol was burned by the British during the War of 1812. Surviving volumes from Jefferson's library are available for use in the Rare Book and Special Collections Division of the Library of Congress. His library served as the foundation for the national library's diverse collections.

INTRODUCTION

The Library and the Catalog

One of Thomas Jefferson's most avid lifelong interests was his library. His first collection of books was largely destroyed by fire in 1770, but the twenty-six-year-old lawyer immediately set out to replace it with a more extensive library, one that would encompass virtually the whole of recorded knowledge. And in spite of the disruptions of the ensuing revolution, Jefferson noted in 1783 that he had acquired the remarkable total of 2,640 volumes. When he departed the following year for Europe he looked forward to greatly expanding his library, and, whenever he was not carrying out his duties as the American minister to France, he haunted the Parisian booksellers and frequently placed orders with book dealers in London and other European cities. On returning to America in 1789 he possessed a library twice the size of the one he had owned at his departure. By 1815, he had a collection of 6,700 volumes.

But it was not so much on the size of his library that Jefferson prided himself as on the fact that the books it contained had been chosen with great care. He realized that the combination of his intense love of books, his extensive travels, his keen knowledge of bibliography, and his ample means had provided him unique opportunities as a collector to acquire a library that was unrivaled in America. At some point Jefferson decided that this splendid library should not remain private property, thinking at first that he might donate it to a university. But when the congressional library in Washington was burned by the invading British army in 1814, the former president promptly offered his own. Though he was then in serious financial straits, Jefferson's primary purpose was to assure that the nation's legislators had access to the best sources of information and ideas, for he said that he would accept whatever price and terms of payment Congress thought appropriate as long as the entire collection was purchased. Though the debate was partisan and often rancorous, Congress approved the purchase of the collection in early 1815 for $23,950.

In March, only weeks before Jefferson's books were to be hauled in wagons from Monticello to Washington, George Watterston was appointed Librarian of Congress by President James Madison on the recommendation of Joseph Milligan, the Georgetown bookseller who had appraised Jefferson's books for Congress. Watterston's most pressing duty was to oversee the transfer of the

Jefferson books and to install them in the temporary Capitol building. He later wrote that he single-handedly labeled and arranged the books on shelves when they arrived in Washington.[1]

When Jefferson offered his library to Congress in September 1814, he sent along his handwritten catalog for the inspection of the congressional library committee. Not only did this catalog arrange the books in subject categories, but the categories themselves were part of an overall classification scheme that was adapted from the second book of Francis Bacon's *The Advancement of Learning.* "One of the most systematic of men," Dumas Malone has written of Jefferson, "he was in character as a cataloguer."[2] Perhaps no activity so represents the man and his distinctive mentality as the cataloging and classification of books.

In *The Advancement of Learning,* Bacon had organized all knowledge into the categories of Memory, Reason, and Imagination. Memory was divided into four parts: natural (which consisted of technology and information about inanimate and animate things), civil, ecclesiastical, and literary. Reason was broken down into divine, natural, and civil sections. Lastly, Imagination was arranged according to narrative, representative (drama), and parabolical (allegory). Jefferson renamed Bacon's three categories History, Philosophy, and the Fine Arts. In the section devoted to History, Jefferson relegated Bacon's major division of Ecclesiastical History to a subsection of Civil History and eliminated altogether the section reserved for literary matters. In Philosophy, he combined Bacon's Civil and Divine Reason categories into a new division entitled Moral Philosophy. His treatment of theological and ecclesiastical subjects stems from his distrust of organized religions. On the other hand, Jefferson expanded Bacon's Imagination section into a Fine Arts category that embraced not only literary works but also such decorative and fine arts as gardening, painting, architecture, and music.

Jefferson added a further dimension to Bacon's scheme by creating forty-four chapters, as he termed them, that identified specific subjects. Some chapters dealt with areas such as chemistry that were unknown in Bacon's time. Jefferson saw this elaborate arrangement not as a rigid system but as a flexible model adaptable to the exigencies of time and circumstance. Since during his own life he was deeply involved in political and legal matters, these sections in his classification scheme were necessarily very detailed. He allowed that a physician or theologian, having acquired a different kind of library, would have created different chapters.

To twentieth-century eyes, parts of Jefferson's classification may seem puzzling. It is no surprise to find categories such as Modern British History under the broad division of History, but such unexpected subjects as Agriculture, Surgery, and Natural History also appear there. The second broad category, Philosophy, combines subjects such as Mechanics, the Law of Nature and Nations, Politics, Phonics, and Arithmetic. Today's reader might sensibly ask not only what Agriculture and Modern British History have in common but also how Mechanics and the Law of Nature and Nations can both be related to what we call Philosophy.

To pursue these questions is to confront Jefferson's world and his world view. History, the first of his three major categories, was composed of all known facts about the physical universe. This universe consisted of what could be learned about human activity through time (Civil History) and what had been discovered about the nature of plants, animals, and minerals (Natural History). Understanding the historical dimension of any subject was crucial to a meaningful comprehension of the present. A fact discovered long ago was no less valid than one recently established. If History dealt with the known world, Philosophy was concerned with the laws that governed those facts—the Moral for human affairs and the Mathematical for the forces of nature.

Keeping in mind the meaning of the general organizational principles when looking at specific chapters helps explain the sometimes apparently strange juxtapositions. Anatomy is composed of all the known facts about the human body just as Antient History is composed of all known facts about the classical world. This common link explains why they are both found under History. By the same token, Law Ecclesiastical governs religious communities just as the rules of Geometry govern the relationships of circles, triangles, and other such figures. Consequently, both Law Ecclesiastical and Geometry are found under Philosophy.

The catalog that Jefferson sent to Washington was particularly important because it presented the books within the forty-four chapters in a meaningful order. This order Jefferson described as "sometimes analytical, sometimes chronological, & sometimes a combination of both."[3] This ordering of the chapters and of the individual books within each chapter is a detailed and telling product of Jefferson's distinctive imagination at work and has been aptly described by Arthur Bestor as "a blueprint of his own mind."[4]

After the books were unpacked and set up in Washington, Librarian George Watterston corresponded with Jefferson about the form the printed catalog that Congress had authorized should take. There was no standard method for organizing book catalogs at the time, though most printed library catalogs of the period arranged titles either according to the size of the volumes or in broad subject categories. Another method was alphabetical by author or title, but Jefferson wrote Watterston that he found this "very unsatisfactory, because of the medley it presents to the mind, the difficulty sometimes of re-calling an author's name, and the greater difficulty, where the name is not given, of selecting the word in the title, which shall determine its alphabetical place."[5] But Watterston's printed catalog, which appeared in 1815, struck a compro-mise. While it preserved Jefferson's classification and kept the books in the chapters he had assigned, it alphabetized the entries within the chapters and therefore destroyed Jefferson's carefully worked-out, sometimes analytical, sometimes chronological order.[6]

Watterston was probably unaware of the care with which Jefferson had ordered the entries in the catalog. In his novel *Wanderer in Washington,* Watter-ston expressed his genuine admiration for the former President: "Mr. Jefferson's was a constitution of iron; he could act and reflect more than any man I ever saw, without being fatigued or exhausted. . . . He lived like a philosopher."[7] But Jefferson had not given his collection a detailed arrangement as a casual exercise in philosophical taxonomy. The arrangement was very important to him, and he objected to Watterston's changes in a letter to Joseph Cabell: "The form of the catalogue has been much injured in the publication; for although they have preserved my division into chapters, they have reduced the books in each chap-ter to alphabetical order, instead of the chronological or analytical arrangements I had given them."[8]

The handwritten catalog that Jefferson had sent to Congress along with his library was retained by Watterston, who claimed it as his personal property when he was dismissed from the post of Librarian of Congress in 1829. It has never been located by scholars, and its disappearance has meant that the ar-rangement of individual books that was so important to Jefferson has been lost. In the meantime, Jefferson's library has become the object of great interest for the light it sheds on one of America's most remarkable men. Adrienne Koch observed in her book *The Philosophy of Thomas Jefferson:* "Since his library was the product of extraordinary devotion and, as he said, 'handpicked,' it is a val-uable index to his intellectual attachments."[9]

In view of this kind of interest and in tribute to its Jeffersonian origins, the Library of Congress sponsored an annotated catalog of the great library that

4

Jefferson sold to Congress in 1815. It was compiled by E. Millicent Sowerby and published by the Library in five large volumes between 1952 and 1959. The *Catalogue of the Library of Thomas Jefferson* listed the abbreviated entries given in the 1815 printed catalog edited by Watterston, tried to establish a full bibliographic entry for each work, and gathered anything Jefferson had written to correspondents about each book. When it was published, Sowerby's work was heralded by Douglass Adair of the *William and Mary Quarterly* as a "major event in the field of Jefferson studies."

In this biobibliography, as she termed it, Sowerby arranged the books according to Jefferson's chapters. She realized the importance of the manuscript that Watterston had retained, however, and attempted to restore the order of the books within each chapter by using another manuscript catalog of his library that Jefferson had composed much before the one he sent to Washington in 1814.[10] This earlier catalog is a densely interlined and worked over manuscript dated 1783 that is now in the collections of the Massachusetts Historical Society. Sowerby's promising plan miscarried, not only because of the difficulty of fathoming the intended order in certain heavily revised parts of this manuscript but also because Jefferson had made extensive changes in compiling the later version of the catalog that he sent to Washington with his library. Many books sold to Congress were not in the 1783 catalog. Jefferson also condensed the forty-six chapters in the earlier manuscript into forty-four in the one he sent to Congress. In the foreword to volume 4 of the *Catalogue of the Library of Thomas Jefferson,* Miss Sowerby was forced to admit ruefully that her plan to establish Jefferson's original order for the books had failed.

Jefferson's Order Restored

The catalog of Jefferson's library contained in the pages that follow presents the entries in an order assigned by Jefferson. The restoration of Jefferson's order has been made possible by the rediscovery of a manuscript that was commissioned and corrected by Jefferson for the purpose of reconstructing the original catalog order that had been obliterated in Watterston's printed congressional catalog of 1815. This manuscript has an unusual provenance and an obscure history. It was donated to the Library of Congress in 1917 by Frank Goodell, who had found it in the library of which he was in charge at Camp Wheeler in Georgia. For many years, it was mistakenly labeled as a catalog of the library at the University of Virginia[11] and may have been intended for its collections. Bound with the manuscript catalog, which was clearly not in Jefferson's hand, was a copy of the 1815 printed catalog. The volume donated by Goodell remained in the Library's Manuscript Division until 1954 when it was transferred to the Rare Book and Special Collections Division. There it rested uncataloged and virtually unnoticed at the end of the library that Jefferson had sold in 1815.[12] A close comparison of the manuscript and the 1815 printed catalog makes clear, however, that the two contain the same entries, though each is arranged in a different order.

Not much is known about the early history of the manuscript, but it appears to have been prepared for Jefferson at his request in 1823 by Nicholas P. Trist, the young man who would eventually become his grandson-in-law and private secretary. It is not surprising that Jefferson's thoughts should have turned to book catalogs in 1823 since he was then actively engaged in organizing the University of Virginia library. The manuscript is in handwriting and on paper that perfectly match those of the commonplace book Trist kept in the summer and fall of 1823,[13] and its origin is confirmed by an exchange of letters. Writing to Jefferson from Louisiana on October 18, 1823, Trist says: "I avail myself of the first opportunity that offers to return your catalogue, the absence of which will have proved, I fear, a greater inconvenience than can be compensated by the copy I have made."[14] Jefferson replied on his eighty-first birthday, April 13, 1824: "The catalogues, printed and ms. were safely received. the last has given you more trouble than I ought to have subjected you to. it is very precious to me, and I am truly thankful to you for it."[15] The remarks suggest that Jefferson had sent to Trist a copy of the 1815 printed catalog that he had annotated to indicate his intended order for the books. Trist then compiled the manuscript catalog that is published here and sent it, along with Jefferson's annotated copy of the printed catalog, back to Jefferson when the job was completed. Though Jefferson's marked 1815 printed catalog has not been found and is presumed lost, we now have the Trist manuscript copy that was precious to Jefferson because it reclaimed the results of an important undertaking that had nearly been lost—his painstaking and distinctive ordering of the books in his magnificent library. It is printed here for the first time.

The chapters, as has been noted, are subject categories and are themselves arranged in a significant order that constitutes an overall classification scheme. Jefferson followed conventional eighteenth-century bibliographical format to describe each title listed within the chapters, providing concise information on the author, title, number of volumes, and size. A typical entry from the first chapter (Antient History) reads:

114. Middleton's life of Cicero 2 v. 4°.

This signifies a two-volume life of Cicero by Conyers Middleton published in quarto. Quarto refers to the size of the volume. Folio books are the largest, quarto the next largest, and octavo and duodecimo follow in descending order. For some books, information about language, edition, and place and date of publication is also supplied:

6. Appolodorus. Gr. Lat. Heyne, 4 v 12° Goettingae, 1782

This work is a four-volume duodecimo edition of Apollodorus in both Greek and Latin edited by Christian Heyne and published in Goettingen in 1782. The small *p* before the size of certain volumes, such as the first entry in chapter 7, indicates that the volume is *petit* or a smaller format than usual. Thus "p folio" shows that the book is a folio but smaller than most other folios.

The initial number assigned to each entry refers not to its catalog order but to its shelf position. The numerical sequence began anew with each chapter.[16] In Jefferson's bookcases in Monticello, the smaller books, such as the duodecimos, were put on the upper shelves; the middle-sized quartos and octavos were on ranges below them; and the folios were stored on the bottom shelves. In this way, the books in each chapter were kept together on Jefferson's shelves, and at the same time he was able to take advantage of the economies of space afforded by shelving according to size. In the first chapter, for example, the numbering sequence works out as follows:

1–16	duodecimos
17–101	octavos
102–115	quartos
116–129	folios

A few entries begin with letters rather than numbers. These books were particularly large and must have been kept separately.

To refer to earlier examples, Middleton's life of Cicero (no. 114) is positioned with the quartos on one of the middle shelves of the bookcase devoted to Antient History, and Heyne's edition of Appollodorus (no. 6) would be found near the beginning of the duodecimos at the top. Thus the numbering (and arrangement) of the books on the shelves was perfectly orderly, though in the catalog it appeared chaotic. As Jefferson explained the system to Watterston,

"On every book is a label, indicating the chapter of the catalogue to which it belongs, and the order it holds among those of the same format. So that, although the numbers seem confused on the catalogue, they are consecutive on the volumes as they stand on their shelves, and indicate at once the place they occupy there."[17]

Jefferson's catalog order, which his commission to Trist shows he was at pains to reestablish, relates then to the content of the books rather than to their size or shelf order. In listing the books in his catalog, he sought to place them in an order that reflected their relationship to their subject and to each other, either historically or by some other analytical connection. Such a catalog enables one not only to see the books of his great library as Jefferson wanted us to see them but also to learn something about his characteristic perceptions and to witness the distinctive ways in which he conceptualized historical developments and intellectual phenomena. This is what Arthur Bestor meant when he referred to Jefferson's catalog as a "blueprint" of his mind.

In the ordering of his books on American geography, for example, Jefferson varies the chronological and analytical aspects of his arrangement in telling ways, to which no description can do justice. His chief coordinates are chronological (early-to-late) and directional (North-to-South), giving the appearance of a systematic, objective approach. But his weaving of topics and titles, far from being obvious or straightforward, is artful and deft. For instance, the principal account of the Lewis and Clark expedition, which he himself promoted in the nineteenth century, is prominently positioned in the early part of the chapter with works on Indians and North American exploration. The accounts of La Salle's important seventeenth-century expeditions and books about Louisiana are placed much further on, precisely the reverse of what one might logically expect. To take another example, though the Spanish were first in the New World, Jefferson had the books about their American ventures and the states that emerged in these areas come last in this chapter of his catalog.

The architecture chapter is of particular interest. In the *Catalogue of the Library of Thomas Jefferson,* Sowerby arranged these books roughly by imprint date. The earliest, such as Vitruvius's *Les dix livres d'architecture* (1684), are placed at the beginning of the chapter and later publications, such as Friedrich Meinert's *Die Schöne Landbaukunst* (1798), are at the end. This arrangement totally obscures Jefferson's belief that a knowledge of the rules of classical architecture was the most essential guide in constructing modern buildings, whereas the Trist manuscript clearly reveals Jefferson's deep respect for the classical tradition. In Trist's manuscript copy of Jefferson's catalog, the architecture chapter begins with relatively recent books that describe the existing ruins of Greece and Rome, suggesting that these extant buildings should be the models for all the structures that followed. The listing then continues by giving the titles of books whose authors attempted to reconstruct classical monuments and buildings that no longer existed and works that explained the theory of Greek and Roman building design. The chapter then leads up to Vitruvius and Palladio, whom Jefferson valued as the best interpreters of antiquity. Jefferson completed the architecture chapter by listing treatises on practical aspects of architecture that were in use in America. The deep respect for the classical tradition that is demonstrated in this section also extended to many of his other interests. After retiring from public service in 1809, Jefferson considered reading the Latin and Greek classics in their original languages to be one of his most cherished activities.

The geography and architecture chapters from the 1815 printed catalog have been reproduced in facsimile at the end of this book as representative examples so that the reader may conveniently compare their arrangement of the Jefferson books with the order offered in the Trist manuscript.

The usefulness of the Trist manuscript to those interested in Jefferson's life is clear. He once observed to John Adams that he could not live without books. In fact, Jefferson's reading seems to have informed so many of his activities that close attention to the books in his library offers useful insights to students of almost any aspect of his multifaceted career. The order in which he placed his books will of course also be of interest to students of broader topics, such as the Enlightenment in America.

In a wider symbolic sense, this catalog catches America at one of its most characteristically hopeful moments. Americans living at the end of the eighteenth century were infused with an exciting sense of freedom that encouraged them to experiment with the social and political orders. The new beginning represented by the independence the Colonies wrested from Great Britain would offer the opportunity for the citizens of the new Republic to winnow out the errors of the European tradition that repressed the natural human instinct toward self-betterment that many Americans believed to be present in all segments of society. During his lifetime as a dedicated reader, Jefferson constantly sifted through world literature seeking those books that contained information and ideas that might benefit his country. This catalog presents the distillation of the efforts by one of America's leading intellectuals to organize the knowledge of the Old World so as to make it useful for the New. Jefferson's efforts in this area are a testament to his belief that knowledge and the unobstructed access to ideas are necessary tools for social improvement. As such, his library not only offers a key to his own thinking but also symbolizes an admirable and important part of the cultural tradition of the American society he envisioned and helped to found.

James Gilreath
Library of Congress

Douglas L. Wilson
Knox College

Notes

1. George Watterston, "Memorandum," George Watterston Papers, box 2, Manuscript Division, Library of Congress.
2. Dumas Malone, *The Sage of Monticello* (Boston: Little, Brown and Company, 1981), 169.
3. Jefferson to George Watterston, 7 May 1815, quoted in E. Millicent Sowerby, ed., *Catalogue of the Library of Thomas Jefferson,* 5 vols. (Washington: Library of Congress, 1952–59), 5:218.
4. Arthur E. Bestor, "Thomas Jefferson and the Freedom of Books," in *Three Presidents and Their Books* (Urbana: University of Illinois Press, 1955), 6.
5. Jefferson to George Watterston, 7 May 1815, quoted in William Dawson Johnston, *History of the Library of Congress* (Washington: U.S. Government Printing Office, 1904), 144.
6. Library of Congress, *Catalogue of the Library of the United States* (Washington: Printed by Jonathan Elliot, 1815).
7. George Watterston, *Wanderer in Washington* (Washington: Jonathan Elliot, 1827), 57.
8. Jefferson to Joseph C. Cabell, 2 February 1816, Andrew A. Lipscomb and Albert Ellery Bergh, eds., *The Writings of Thomas Jefferson,* 20 vols. (Washington: Thomas Jefferson Memorial Association, 1903–4), 14:418.
9. Adrienne Koch, *The Philosophy of Thomas Jefferson* (New York: Columbia University Press, 1943), xiii.
10. Sowerby, *Catalogue of the Library of Thomas Jefferson,* 1:ix.
11. The label on the cover of the volume, presumably affixed after its acquisition by the Library of Congress, reads: "University of Virginia / Catalogue of the library. With two / Ms. corrections by Thos. Jefferson. / Autograph document, Followed by print- / ed copy of the Library of Congress cata- / logue, 1815." Despite the assertion on the label that Jefferson made two corrections in Trist's manuscript, the editors have been able to identify positively only one emendation in Jefferson's hand (see page 14).
12. The manuscript and the printed catalog have now received Library of Congress cataloging and are available in the Rare Book and Special Collections Division by call number.
13. Nicholas P. Trist Papers, box 14, Manuscript Division, Library of Congress.
14. Nicholas Trist to Jefferson, 18 October 1823, Thomas Jefferson Papers, Manuscript Division, Library of Congress.

15. Jefferson to Nicholas Trist, 13 April 1824, Jefferson Papers, property of the Thomas Jefferson Memorial Foundation in the custody of the Manuscript Department, Alderman Library, University of Virginia. The editors thank Ruth Lester of the Papers of Thomas Jefferson for calling this letter to their attention.
16. An exception is chapter 16, Ethics, a very long chapter, in which the two major divisions, Moral Philosophy and the Law of Nature and Nations, are numbered separately.
17. Johnston, *History of the Library,* 144.

Selected Reading List

The richest source of information on the library Jefferson sold to Congress in 1815 is the monumental compilation by E. Millicent Sowerby, *Catalogue of the Library of Thomas Jefferson,* 5 vols. (Washington: Library of Congress, 1952–59). Begun as a straightforward listing of the books, the project grew to encompass full bibliographical descriptions, annotations regarding the circumstances of acquisitions and other matters, and extensive quotations from Jefferson's correspondence on relevant books and authors. Under the auspices of the Thomas Jefferson Memorial Foundation, this invaluable catalog has been reprinted by the University Press of Virginia (1983).

In spite of its many virtues, Sowerby's catalog does have limitations and shortcomings that can present serious problems for the unwary student of Jefferson's library. These are described and discussed in two articles by the present editors: James Gilreath, "Sowerby Revirescent and Revised," *Papers of the Bibliographical Society of America* 78 (1984): 19–32; and Douglas L. Wilson, "Sowerby Revisited: The Unfinished Catalogue of Jefferson's Library," *William and Mary Quarterly,* 3d series, 41 (1984): 615–28.

An essay that deals comprehensively with all of Jefferson's libraries is Douglas L. Wilson, "Jefferson's Library," in *Thomas Jefferson: A Reference Biography,* ed. Merrill D. Peterson (New York: Charles Scribners Sons, 1986), 157–80.

The most detailed and well-documented account of the sale and transfer of Jefferson's library to Congress, with pertinent information on Librarian Watterston and the 1815 catalog, is William Dawson Johnston, *History of the Library of Congress* (Washington: U.S. Government Printing Office, 1904), 68–104. Dumas Malone's chapter, "Books in Transit: The Library of Congress," on pages 169–84 of *The Sage of Monticello* (Boston: Little, Brown and Company, 1981), is a readable and readily available account of the transfer. Also interesting is *Thomas Jefferson and the World of Books,* from a symposium held at the Library of Congress on September 21, 1976, which includes comments by Daniel Boorstin, Dumas Malone, Frederick Goff, and Merrill Peterson.

A valuable study of Jefferson as a library classifier is Leo E. LaMontagne, *American Library Classification, with Special Reference to the Library of Congress* (Hamden, Conn.: Shoe String Press, 1961), 27–60. Finally, an admirable discussion of Jefferson's use of a significant portion of his library is H. Trevor Colbourn's essay "Thomas Jefferson's Use of the Past," in the *William and Mary Quarterly,* 3d series, 15 (1958): 56–70.

Editorial Note

The editors' aim has been to present the text of the catalog as it appears in the Trist manuscript. Not only was Nicholas Trist himself a very good copyist, knowledgeable and conscientious, but there is evidence that Jefferson proofread the manuscript and numbered its pages. Trist was, however, quite careless about punctuation and clearly made no effort to follow copy (that is, Jefferson's marked copy of the 1815 printed catalog) exactly or to be consistent in regard to punctuation from entry to entry. We have emulated Jefferson's example and have made no attempt to reimpose the punctuation of his original on Trist's transcription. In so doing, we have acted in accordance with another aim, which was to minimize the editorial apparatus.

But the temptations that beset editors are often irresistible, and we here confess that we have yielded to the enticements of emendation in a few instances.

(1) We have made only one correction, and that where the text exhibited an obvious copying error that might cause the reader confusion. This is duly listed at the end of this section.

(2) On a few occasions, Trist left out an entry by mistake and supplied it at the bottom of the page with an asterisk to indicate where it should have gone. In such cases we have simply printed the entry in its rightful place.

(3) Where the binder has cropped part of an entry, we have supplied the cropped material within square brackets from the 1815 catalog.

(4) We have regularized the length of the long dashes, some of which are very long indeed in Trist's copy.

(5) Matter that was entered and then crossed out by Trist has been omitted.

CORRECTION by the EDITORS:

Chapter 29: No. 61 is misnumbered 161 in the manuscript.

CORRECTION in JEFFERSON'S HAND:

On page 109 in entry 26, Jefferson has crossed out "Inigo Jones'" (which the editors have restored within angle brackets) and inserted "Ld. Burlington's."

This is a strange entry. *The Architecture of A. Palladio* is the first complete English edition of Palladio's work and was published in 1715 by Giacomo Leoni. Though Inigo Jones's notes were advertised as being included in this edition, they did not appear until the 1742 edition. Jefferson's notation, however, may refer instead to *The Four Books of Andrea Palladio's Architecture* published by Isaac Ware in London in 1738, which was both dedicated to Lord Burlington and translated by him. Richard Boyle, the third earl of Burlington, was an important force in the early eighteenth century in the movement to instill the principles of the Italian Renaissance in English architects. The illustrations in the 1738 Ware edition faithfully followed the original woodblocks from the 1570 Italian edition and the publisher took pains in other ways to reflect the integrity of the first edition. In contrast, Leoni's 1715 and 1742 versions used copperplate engravings that, though they are based on the 1570 woodblocks, distort the proportions of the illustrations.

Jefferson probably would have appreciated the Burlington-Ware collaboration to preserve the classical purity of their edition of Palladio's work. On the other hand, in at least one other instance Jefferson simply confused Burlington and Jones. In a February 28, 1804, letter to Benjamin Latrobe that is cited on page 360 of volume 4 in Millicent Sowerby's *Catalogue of the Library of Thomas Jefferson,* Jefferson wrote: "Ld. Burlington in his notes on Palladio tells us that he found most of the buildings erected under Palladio's direction & described in his architecture to have their columns made of brick in this way and covered over with stucco." No such information is included in Isaac Ware's edition of *The Four Books of Andrea Palladio's Architecture,* but it does appear in one of Jones's notes in the 1742 edition of *The Architecture of A. Palladio.* Whether or not Jefferson once again made the error of confusing Burlington and Jones when correcting the Trist manuscript is not certain.

Thomas Jefferson's
Catalogue

Catalogue.

1   Memory

Chapter 1
History — Civil.
Ancient History.

1. Berosus, Manetho, Xenophontis equivoca. Fabius Pictor, Myrsilus, Cato de originibus, antonini itinerarium, Sempronii Italia, Metasthenes, Philo de temporibus, annii Viterbensis Chronographia, aretii Sicilia et Hispania. 12° antwerp 1545.

1ᵗ. Sanchoniathon's Phenician History, by Cumberland. 8°
2   Manethon. Dynasties de par le comte Jean Potocki. 12°
    Manethon. Chronologie de par Potocki. 4°
    Potocki. Principes de chronologie anterieures aux olympriades. 4°
3   Perizonius. aegyptiarum originum investigatio. 12°
    Perizonius. Babilonica et aegyptiaca originee. 12°
    Josephus. Gr. Lat. Bernardi. fol.
58 Josephus. Gr. Lat. Havrcampii et Hudsonii. edente Oberthur. 6. v. 8°.
117 Josephus. Eng. by Whiston. fol.
    Decreta Romanorum pro Judaeis facta. Krebsii. 8° Lipsiae 1768.
5   Historiae poeticae scriptores antiqui, Sc. Apollodorus. Conon, Ptolomaeus Hephaest: F. Partha-
•   nius, Antoninus Liberalis, Gr. Lat. Gale, 8° p.
6   Apollodorus Gr. Lat. Heyne. 2 v 12° Goettingae, 1782.
    Herodotus. Gr. Lat. Gronovii. 9 v 12°. Foulis.
    Thucydides. Gr. Lat. Wasse et Dukeri. 8 v 12°. Foulis.
118 Thucydides. Gr. Lat. not. var. Dukeri, fol.
    Thucydides. translated by Hobbes. fol.
24 Thucydides. Eng. by Smith. 2 v. 4°
9   Xenophontis Hellenica et agesilaus. Gr. Lat. Wells 4 v 12°. Foulis.
    Xenophontis Cyri expeditio et Hipparchicos, Gr. Lat. Hutchinson 4 v 12°. Foulis.
    Do. Eng. by Spelman. 2 v. 8°
11 Xenophontis Cyropaedia. Gr. Lat. Hutchinson, 4 v 12°. Foulis.
103 Xenophontis Cyropaedia. Gr. Lat. Hutchinson. 4°
106 Mitford's history of Greece 4 v 4°
120 arriani expeditio alexandri, Gr. Lat. Vulcanii. fol. Stephanus, 1575.

The first page of Nicholas Trist's manuscript, prepared for Jefferson in 1823. Jefferson's original manuscript catalog of the library he sold to Congress—with the entries ordered according to his classification of knowledge—was lost when George Watterston kept it after being dismissed from the post of Librarian of Congress. Jefferson subsequently commissioned Nicholas P. Trist to reconstruct the catalog.

16

Catalogue

I   Memory

Chapter 1
History—Civil
Antient History.

1. Berosus, Manetho, Xenophontis equivoca, Fabius Pictor, Myrsilus, Cato de originibus, Antonini itinerarium, Sempronii Italia, Metasthenes, Philo de temporibus, Annii Viterbensis Chronographia, Aretii Sicilia et Hispania. 12° Antwerp 1545.
57. Sanchoniathon's Phenician History, by Cumberland. 8°
2. Manethon, Dynasties de par le comte Jean Potocki. 12°
102. Manethon, Chronologie de par Potocki. 4°
103. Potocki, Principes de Chronologie antérieures aux Olympiades. 4°
3. Perizonius. Aegyptiarum originum investigatio 12°
4. Perizonius. Babilonicae et Aegyptiacae origines. 12°
116. Josephus. Gr. Lat. Bernardi. fol
58. Josephus. Gr. Lat. Havercampii et Hudsonii, edente Oberthiir. 6. v. 8°.
117. Josephus, Eng. by Whiston. fol.
59. Decreta Romanorum pro Judaeis facta. Krebsii. 8° Lipsiae 1768.
5. Historiae poeticae scriptores antiqui, sc Apollodorus, Conon, Ptolomaeus Hephaest, F. Parthenius, Antoninus Liberalis, Gr. Lat. Gale, 8° p.
6. Apollodorus. Gr. Lat. Heyne, 4 v 12° Goettingae, 1782
7. Herodotus, Gr. Lat. Gronovii. 9 v 12°, Foulis
8. Thucydides, Gr. Lat. Wassii et Dukeri, 8 v 12°, Foulis
118. Thucydides. Gr. Lat. not. var. Dukeri, fol
119. Thucydides. translated by Hobbes. fol
104. Thucydides. Eng. by Smith. 2 v 4°
9. Xenophontis Hellenica et Agesilaus. Gr. Lat. Wells 4 v 12°, Foulis

10. Xenophontis Cyri expeditio et Hipparchicos, Gr. Lat. Hutchinson 4 v 12°, Foulis
60. D°   Eng by Spelman, 2 v. 8°
11. Xenophontis Cyropaedia. Gr. Lat. Hutchinson, 4 v 12°. Foulis
105. Xenophontis Cyropaedia. Gr. Lat. Hutchinson. 4°.
106. Mitford's history of Greece 4 v 4°
120. Arriani expeditio Alexandri. Gr. Lat. Vulcanii, fol. Stephanus, 1575.
61. Arriani expeditio Alexandri. Gr. Lat. Raphelii. 8° Wetstenii. 1767
62. Quintus Curtius. Not. var. 8° Elzevir
63. Id.   In usum Delphini cum Supplemento Frienshemii 8°
12. Quintus Curtius, Maittaire 12°
13. Quinte Curce. Lat Fran. de Vaugelas 12°
64. Blackwell's life and writings of Homer, and court of Augustus. 8°
107. Diogenes Laertius, Gr. Lat. Meibomii. 2 v. 4°
14. Diogenes Laertius et Eunapius, Gr. Lat. 2. v. 12°
15. Diogène de Laerce. 2 v 12°. Paris 1668
108. Stanley's lives of the Philosophers, 4°
65. Justin, not. var. 2 v. 8°.
66. Id. Delphini, 8°
121. Diodori Siculi libri XV de XL Gr. Stephani 1559 fol.
16. Diodori Siculi libri 16, 17, 18, 19, 20, Gr. Basiliae et Lat Rhodomanni, 4 v. 12°.
67. Stanyan's Grecian history. 2 v. 8°
68. Anacharsis, voyage d'. en Grece, par Barthélemy. 8 v. 8°.
69. Potter's Antiquities of Greece, 2 v. 8°.
122. Athenaei Deipnosophistae, Lat. Natale de Conte, fol
109. Bryant's Mythology. 3 v. 4°.
17. Horatii Tursellini historiae universalis epitomen. 12°.
110. Perizonii commentarii in epitomen Horat. Tursellini. 3 v. 4° M.S.
18. Perizonii animadversiones historicae, 12°.
70. Dionysii Halicarnensis opera omnia, not. var. Gr. Lat. 6. v. 8°, Lipsiae, 1774.
19. Id. Quae extant. Lat. p. 8° Hanoviae 1615.
111. Denys d'Halacarnasse. 2 v 4°.
123. Polybii historia Gr. Lat. Casauboni fol
71. Id. Gr. Lat. Casauboni. not. var. Gronovii et Ernesti. Lipsiae 1764. & Eng by Hampton. 8. v. 8°.

18

20. Livius supplementis Freinshemii et notis Joan. Clerici, Watsteni. 10 v. 12°.

112. Livius Dujatii, in usum Delphini, 5 v. 4°.—

124. Livio del Nardi. 3. v. fol

72. Sallust Wasseii, not. var. et Julius Exuperantius, 4° p.

73. Id.   Delphini 8°.

21. Id.   Foulis. 12°

22. Id.   Maittaire 12°.—

74. Caesar, notis Davisii et variorum, Metaphrasi Graeca, Cant 1727 2 v 8°

75. Id.   Delphini, 8°

23. Id.   Fr. de d'Ablancourt 12°

76. Florus not. var. 2 v 8°

77. Id.   Delphini, 8°

78. Id.   Stirling, 8°.

24. Id.   Lat. Fr. Le Mothe, La Vayer, 12°

25. Vertot, Révolutions de Rome 3 v. 12°.

26. Macquer, Annales Romaines par, 12°

113. Plutarchi vitae. Gr. Lat. Cruserii, 4 v. p. fol

27. Id.   Gr. Lat. Eng. 13 v. 12°

28. Cornelius Nepos, Cruserii, 12°

79. Id.   Notis varior. 8°

29. Id.   Lat. Ital. dal Bandiera, 8°, p.

30. Id.   Foulis, 12°.

114. Middleton's life of Cicero 2 v. 4°.

80. Velleius Paterculus, not. var. 8°.

81. Id.   Oxoniæ, 8°

125. Dionis cassii historia et Xiphilinus. Gr. Lat. Xylandri. fol

82. Appiani Alexandrini historia, Gr. Lat. Tollii. 2 v 8° Jansonii, 1670

31. Appiano Alessandrino dal Braccio e Ruscelli, 12° Ven. 1567

83. Tacitus Cronovii, not var. Elzevir, 1672 and Eng. by Gordon, 9 v 8°.

32. Tacitus. edition of Brotier with Span. por Sveyro, and Eng. by Gordon, 12 v. p 8°.

84. Suetonius Delphini. 8°

85. Scriptores VI Historiae Augustae, Sc: Aelius Spartianus, Julius Capitolinus, Aelius Lampridius, Vulcatius Gallicanus, Trebellius Pollio. et Flavius Vopiscus. 2 v. 8°

115. Xiphilinus Gr. Lat. Blanci, 2 v. 4°.

86. Orosius p 4° Paris 1506.

33. Herodianus. Gr. Lat. Eng. 2 v. 12°
34. Biographia Classica 2 v. 12°.
35. Juliani Imperatioris, Caesares, Gr. Lat 8°. Erlangae. 1785
87. Julian's Select works by Duncombe. 2 v. 8°
36. Life of Julian 12°.
88. Eutropius, cum metaphrasi Graeca Paeanii, item sextus Rufus, Anonymi funebris oratio in Constantinum, et Messala Covinus, not. var. 8°.
126. Ammianus Marcellinus fol
89. Ammianus Ernesti, Lipsiae, 1773, 3 v 8°
90. Zosimus, Gr. Lat. Oxonii, 8°
37. Nicephori Breviarum historicum de rebus gestis ab obitu Mauricii ad Constantinum usque Copronymum. Gr. Lat. Petavii p 8°.
127. Procopii anecdota sive arcana historia, Gr. Lat Alimanni fol.
38. Histoire Romaine de Xiphilin, Zonase et Zosime, par Coussin, 2 v 12°.
39. Histoire de Constantinople de Procope, Agatias, Ménandre, Théophylacte, Simocatte, Nicephore, Léon, Nicephore Bryenne, Anne Comnene, Nycetas, Pachymere, Contacuzene, et Ducas, par Coussin, 8 v 12°.
40. Histoire de l'empire de l'occident d'Eginard, Tegan, Anonymnus, Nitard, Sᵗ Bertin, Luitprand, Witiquind, par Coussin 2 v 12°
90. Chronicon Alexandrinum, Gr. Lat. Raderi, Monachii, 1624, p 4°
41. Frontini Stratagemata Gaesbeeck, 1675, 16, and Ital. Ven. 1537, 12°
42. Le Beau, Histoire du Bas-Empire, 24 v 12°
92. Gibbon's history of the decline and fall of the Roman empire, 13 v 8°
93. Goldsmith's Roman history 2 v. 8°.
94. Aelianus Perizonii, 2 v 8°
95. Valerius Maximus not. var. 8°
96. Polyaeni Stratagemma, Gr. Lat. Vulteii. 8°
43. Lycosthenis Apophthegmata, 2 v. 12°.
97. Historicis Antiquis Collectanea, Gr. Lat. 8°
44. Apophthegmata, Graeca, Latina. Itall. Gall. Hisp. Tunningii. p 8°
45. Dinothi Memorabilia. 12°
46. Lipsii antiquitates Romanae et Fabricii Romae Collatio. Lond. 1692, 12°
98. Kennet's Antiquities of Rome
47. Goldsmith's Essays. 12°.
48. Vie privée des Romains, par D'Arnay, 12°
49. Moeurs et coutumes des Romains, par Bridault 2 v. 12°
99. Tracts in ancient history by Priestly and Fabbroni. 8°

100. Universal history, 20 v. 8°
128. Howel's history of the world, 3 v. fol.
129. Raleigh's history of the world, 2 v. fol.
101. Hearne's System of universal history, 8°
 50. Abrégé chronologique de l'histoire des Empereurs Romains, Richer 2 v. 12°
 51. Abrégé chronologique de l'histoire des Juifs. 12°
 52. Histoire universelle de Bossuet, 2 v. 12°
 53. Essai historique et chronologique de l'abbé Berlié, 12°
 54. Abrégé chronologique de l'histoire ancienne avant Jésus Christ par Lacombe 12°.
 55. Histoire ancienne de Milot, 4 v 12°.
 56. Histoire ancienne de Rollin, 13 v. 12°.

Chapter 2

Modern History.
Foreign

Southern. General Works—Italy, Rome, Florence, Naples, Venice, Spain, Portugal, France.
Northern. General Works—Lapland, Russia, Poland, Hungary, Sweden, Denmark, Prussia, Germany, Flanders, United Netherlands, Switzerland, Geneva.
Turkey, Asia, Africa.

 86. Leçons d'histoire de Volney, 8°
140. Newton's chronology, 4°
  A. Blair's chronology, fol. grand.
159. Helvicus' Chronology. fol
  1. Weeks' Introduction to Chronology. 12°
 87. Priestley's lectures on history 2 v. 8°

2. Priestley's description of his biographical chart, 12°.
88. Priestley's description and chart of biography, 8°
160. Car. Stephani Dictionarium. Historia Geographicum, Poeticum, Lloydii Oxon. 1671 fol.
89. Abridgment of the historical, geographical, chronological and poetical dic., 1ˢᵗ v 8°.
161. Dictionnaire de Bayle, 4 v. fol
162. Dic: de Moreri avec deux suppléments, 10 v fol.
163. Collier's historical dictionary 4 v. fol.
3. Dict: historique et bibliographique par Lavocat. 4 v 12°
90. Dict: historique par une Sociètè de gens de lettres, 9 v. 8°
91. Dict: des hommes marquans de la fin du 18ᵐᵉ siècle. 8°
141. Galeri des hommes illustres de La Platière 4 v. 4°
92. Ditionnaire de Diplomatique, par Dom de Vaynes, 2 v 8°.—
4. The Chronologist of the War 1789–96. 12°
5. Hardie's remembrancer 12°.—
6. Tablettes chronologiques de l'histoire universelle de Langlet du Fresnoy 2 v. 12°
7. Abrégé chronologique de l'histoire universelle, par Hornot, 12°
93. Tableau chronologique de l'histoire de l'Europe de 476 à 1648. 8°.—
8. Introduction à l'histoire de l'univers par Puffendorf, 4 v 12°.
164. Salmon's modern history, 3 v fol
165. Thuani historia. 7 v fol. [1545–1608]
142. De Thou, histoire universelle, avec la suite, par Rigault 11 v 4°
9. Perizonii historia, Seculi Sextidecimi, 12°.
10. Millot histoire moderne. 5 v 12°.—
11. Colvin's historical letters. 12°—
94. Russel's history of modern Europe, 5 v. 8°.—
143. Gazettes de Leyde, 11 v 4° 1781–1793. 4, 5.
166. Istoria d'ltalia del Guicciardini, 2 v. fol.
12. Il Sacco di Roma del Guicciardini, 12°.
95. Roscoe's life of Lorenzo de Medici 3 v 8°
144. Roscoe's life of Leo X. 4 v 4°·—
.— 13. Opere istoriche del Machiavelli, 1st v. 12°
145. Istoria di Napoli del Giannone 5 v 4°.—
167. Rerum Venetarum historio Justiniani, fol
14. Historia de España di Mariana y Miniana, 16 v 12°

15. Expedicion de los Catalanes y Aragoneses contra Turcos et Griegos por Mon: de osona, p 8°.
16. Obras de Stockler 1ˢ v. 12°.
17. Historia del luxo y de las leyes Suntuarias de España por sempere, 2 v. 12°
96. Tracts historical of Philip II & the league, 8°.
18. Abrégé chronologique de l'histoire d'Espagne et de Portugal 2 v 12.°.—
97. Epitome de las historicas Portuguesas, por Feria y Sousa, p 4°
19. Révolutions de Portugal de Vertot, 12°
20. Conjuration de Portugal en 1640. 12°
98. Anecdotes de Pombal. 8°.—
146. Histoire de France du père Daniel 10 v 4°.
21. Histoire de France de Mezeray, 7 v 12° [1ˢᵗ wanting]
22. Histoire de France de Velly   1315   1–7 v   ⎫
           de Vilaret   1314–1466   8–17   ⎬   30 v 12°
           de Garnier   1469–1560   17–30 ⎭
23. Millot histoire de France 3 v 12°
24. Instructions sur l'histoire de France de Vetour, 12°
25. Varila histoire de France de Sᵗ Louis à Charles IX, 9 v 12°
168. Pauli Jovii sui temporis historia fol
169. Histoire de France de Comines fol.
26. Histoire de Henri Le grand, par Préfixe, 12°
99. Istoria delle guerre civili di Francia, del Davila, 5 v 8°.
27. Mémoires de Sully, 8 v 12°
147. Histoire de la guerre des Alpes de 1744, par Sᵗ Simon, 4°
28. Abrégé chronologique de l'histoire de France, par Hénault, 2 v 12°
29. Mémoires du Cardinal de Retz, 5 v 12°
30. Mémoires du Comte de Forbin, 2 v 12°
31. Biographia Gallica 2 v 12°
148. Histoire Militaire du Règne de Louis le grand, par Le Marq. de Quincy. 7 v 4°.
149. Histoire de Turenne, 2 v 4°.
32. Mémoires des Capitaines Français de Brantome, 2 v, 16.
33. Lettres de Louis XIV par Morelly, 2 v. 16
34. Mémoires de Pompadour. 12°—
35. Vie privée de Louis XV 1 v. 12°
36. Mémoires de la comtesse du Barri, 12°
37. Légende de Charles Cardinal de Lorraine, 12°

100. Vie de Voltaire, 8°

38. Mémoires de Voltaire, 12°
(Mémoires de Voltaire écrits par lui-mème, bound up in N°. 103*) printed
*130

101. Soirées de Fernay. 8°

102. Mémoire Sur la vie et les ouvràges de Turgot, par Dupont 8°.

103. Vie de Turgot par Condorcet.

39. Mémoires de Marmontel, 4 v 12°.

104. Tracts in foreign history, to wit Voltaire, Crillon, Mirabeau, La Prusse, Les
Barbaresques, l'abbé de Mably, 8°

105. La Bastille dévoilée 2 v 8°

106a. Histoire de Latude, 8°

106b. An impartial history of the Late Revolution in France, 8°

107. Essai sur la révolution Française par Paganel, 3 v 8°.

108. Révolution de France, par Désodoards, 8°.

40. Abrégé chronologique de la révolution de France, par Désodoards, 1802,
3 v 12°.

150. Histoire de France depuis La révolution de 1789 à 1793, par Toulongeon
2 v 4° à la mort de Robespierre.

41. Moore's journal of 1792 in France, 2 v 12°

109a. Révolutions de France et de Génève par d'Ivernois. 8°.—

109b. Tableau des Pertes des Français par d'Ivernois, 8°.—

110. Mémoires de Dumouriez. 8°.—

42. Réponse de Carnot sur la conjuration du 18 Fructidor, 12°

111. Appel à la postérité par Madame Roland, 2 v 8°.—

112. Coup-d'oeil politique sur le continent par Satadin. 8°.

113. Tableau des opérations de Bonaparte, par Chas. 8°.—

43. Campagne de la Grande Armée (1805) par Castillon. 12°

44. Histoire des Généraux de la Révolution, par Chateauneuf, 5 v. 12°

45. Sketches of the history of France, by an American, 12°

46. Pelloutier, histoire des Celtes, 2 v 12°.—

47. Olai magni gentium Septentrionalium historia, 12°.

48. Histoire des Goths du Jornandes, par Maupertius, 12°

49. Abrégé chronologique de l'histoire du Nord par La combe 2 v 12°

114. Schefferi Laponia. p 4°.—

151. Histoire ancienne du gouvernement de Cherson, par Potocki, 3 v 4°.—

115. Tookes life of Catherine 2. 2 v. 8°.
116. Histoire de Catherine 2, par Castera, 3 v 8°.
117. Mémoires secrèts sur La Russie, Amsterdam, 1800, 2 v. 8°.—
118. Basseville, vie de François Lefort de Russie 8°.
 50. Abrégé chronologique de l'histoire de Pologne. 12°.—
 51. Histoire de Sobieski roi de Pologne par l'abbé Coyer, 2 v 12°.
119. Histoire de l'anarchie et du démembrement de Pologne, par Ruthiere 4. v. 8°
120. Coup d'oeil sur la décadence de la Pologne, par Komarzewski, 8°
 52. Révolutions de Hongrie, 6 v. 12°.—
 53. Loccenii rerum Suecicarum historia, p 8°
 54. Histoire de la dernière guerre de la Suede, de Peleus, p 8°

 55. Histoire de Dannemarc, par Mallet, 6 v 12°.
 56. Lord Molesworth's account of Denmark, 12°
121. Vie de Frédéric II, Roi de Prusse, par Treuttel, 4 v 8°
122. Tableau de la vie et du règne de Frédéric le Grand, par Grimoard, 8°.
123. Traits caractéristiques et anecdotes de Frédéric II, 8°

124. Oeuvres de Frédéric roi de Prusse. 17 v 8°
 57. Tracts of foreign history, to wit, Vie privée du prince Henri de Prusse, apologia por los agotes de Navarra, por de Lardizabel, 12°.
125. Histoire secrete de la cour de Berlin, par Mirabeau, 2 v 8°.
126. Ségur's history of Frederic William II, 3 v 8°.—
127. The Constitution of the Germanic body, 8°.—
 58. Abrégé Chronologique de l'histoire et du droit public d'allemagne par Pfeiffer, 2 v 12°.
 59. Histoire de l'Empire, par le Sieur Heiss, 3 v 12°.
 60. Tableau des révolutions d'allemagne, par de B. 2 v 12°.
152. Robertson's history of Charles V, 3 v. 4°
128. Watson's history of Philip II, 3 v 8°.
129. Watson and Thompson's history of Philip III, 2 v 8°
130. Tracts historical, to wit, Marie Thêrese, et la guerre et traité de Teschen, 8°
 61. Istoria della guerra della Germania inferiore del Conestaggio, 12°

153. Antiquitates Fuldenses, p. fol.

154. Brief account of the hospital of St Elizabeth

170. Grotii Annales et historiae de rebus Belgicis fol

62. Relationi del Cardinal Bentivoglio, Meerbecq, 1632, 12°.

63. Della guerra di Fiandri dal Bentivoglio 1ma parte Colonia 1635, 12°.

64. Dell histoira di Fiandri de Bentivoglio 2da parte Colonia 1636, 12°.

65. Della guerra di Fiandri dal Bentivoglio, 3^a parte, Colonia 1640, 12°.—

171. Strada Histoire de la guerre de Flandres, par du Ryer, 2 v. fol.

66. The same. Lat. 2 v 12°.

67. Guerras de Flandes de Strada, por de Novar, 7 v 12°.

68. Histoire de la guerre de Flandre, par Strada, 2 v 12°.

155. Aitzema's history of the United Netherlands, 1650, 1651, p. fol.

131. De Witt's state of Holland, 8°.

69. Histoire de la Hollande, 1609–1679, par Neuville, 4 v 12°.

132. History of the United Provinces, 1788, London, Johnson, 8°.—

70. Révolution des Provinces-Unies de Mandrillon, 12°.—

71. Vie de De Ruyter, 12°.—

72. Histoire du Prince d'orange de Lamigue, 2 v 12°.—

73. Stanyan's account of Switzerland, 12°.—

133. Tableau des Révolutions de Genève, par d'Ivernois, 2 v 8°.

134. Le Philadelphien à Genève, 8°.

156. Histoire de l'Empire Ottoman par Prince Cantemir, 4°.—

135. Tracts on the Turks, par Peyssonel et Volney, 8°.—

172. Kempfer's history of Japan, Eng. by Scheuchzer fol. 2 v.

136. Du Halde's history of China, 1st vol. 8°.

74. Historia de la conquista de la China por el Tartaro, por Palafox. p 8°.

75. Histoire de Genghizcan, par Petis de la Croix, 12°.

76. Histoire de Timur Bec, par Petis de la Croix, 4 v 12°.

137. Instituts de Tamerlan, par L'Anglès, 8°.

138. Cambridge's history of the war in India, 8°.

158. Parker's evidence of British transactions in the E. Indies. 4°.—

77. Introduction à l'histoire de l'asie, de l'afrique et de l'amérique par la Martinière, 2 v. 12°.—

139. The revolt of Ali Bey, by S. L. Kosmopolitos, 8°.

78. Histoire des Etats Barbaresques, traduite de l'anglais. 2 v 12°.

79. L'Etat de l'empire de Maroc en 1694, par Pidou de St Olon, 12°.

80. Révolutions de Maroc par Brathwaite, traduction. 12°.—
81. Mémoire Sur le royaume de Tunis par St Gervais, 12°.
82. Ray's American Tars in Tripoli, 12°.
83. Etat de Tripoli, Tunis et Algers. 12°
84. Histoire d'Algers, par Lauguier de Tassey, 12°
85. Voyage dans les Etats Barbaresques, 12°.
173. Ludolphus' history of Ethiopia. fol.

Chap. 3

Modern History
British.

 B. Domesday book. 2 v. fol
76. Cambden's Britannia. Eng. by Gibson. 2 v. fol.
22. Cambden's Britannia. Lat. p. 4°
77. Horsley's Britannia. fol
23. Monumenta Anglicana. 4 v. 8°.
24. Verstegan's Antiquities. 8°.
25. Antiquitates Albionensium, Langhorne 8°.
26. Sheringam de Anglorum gentis origine. 8°.
64. Macpherson's introduction to the history of Gr. Britain and Ireland. 4°.
27. Whitaker's refutation of Macpherson' introduction, 8°.
 1. Gildas, Eng. 16.
78. Eadmerus Seldeni. fol.
79. Rerum Britannicarum Scriptores vetustiores et praecipui, Heidelb. 1587, fol. Sc. Galfridus Monumetensis, Ponticus Virunnius, Gildas, Beda, Gulielmus Neubricensis, Joannes Frossardus.
80. Rerum Anglicarum Scriptores post Bedam praecipui, by Saville, fol. Lond. 1596. Sc. Gulielmus Malmsburiensis, Henricus Huntindoniensis, Rogerus Hovedenus, Cronicon Ethelwerdi, Ingulphus.
81. Anglica, Normannica, Hibernica, Cambrica, a veteribus Scripta, in bibliotheca G Cambdeni. fol. Frank. 1603. Sc. Aesserius Menevensis, Anon-

ymus de vita Gulielmi primi, Thomas Walsingham, Thomas de la More. Gulielmus Gemeticensis, Geraldius Cambrensis
82. Historiæ Anglo-Saxonicæ Scriptores X, by Twisden, Selden, Usher and Somner, 2 v. fol London 1652, Sc. Simeon Dunelmensis, Joannes Hagulstadensis, Richardus Hagulstadensis, Alluredus Rievallensis, Radulphus de Diceto, Joannes Bromptonus, Gervasius Dorobornensis, Thomas Stubbs, Gulielmus Thorne, Henricus Knighton.

Temples introduction to the history of England, in his works N° 95
28. Lord Lyttleton's history of Henry II. 1154, 4 v 8°.
83. Brady's history of England, 59 A. C.–1727 2 v. fol.
84. Matthew Paris Lat. by Watts. W. I. 1067—H. III, 1273 fol.
85. Matthaei Westmonasteriensis flores historiarum, 1–1307. fol.
86. History of Edward II, by E. F. written in 1627, 1284–1307, fol.
87. Tyrrel's history of England.–1399. 5 v fol.
88. Habingdon's history of Edward IV. 1461–1483. fol.
65. Moore's life of Richard III, 1483–1485. 4°
66. Walpole's historic doubts of Richard III. 1483–1485. 4°
89. Ld Bacon's history of Henry VII. 1485–1509. fol.
29. Polydorii Virgilii historia angliæ, 1060 A. C.–1538. 8°.
90. L^d. Herbert of Cherbury's history of Henry VIII. 1509–1546, fol.
91. Godwin, Bishop of Hereford's Annals of Henry VIII. E. VI and Mary, 1509–1558. fol.
92. Strype's Annals, 1558–1580. 2 v. fol
93. Speed's history of England, 1060, A. C.–1605. fol.
94. Baker's Chronicle, 1060, A. C.–1625. fol.
30. Osborn's Narrative of Charles First's imprisonment in the isle of Wight, a pamphlet.
 2. Eikon Basilike, p 8°.
 3. A Defence of Eikon Basilike, 12°.
 4. Reliquiæ Sacræ Carolinæ, 1640–1648, 12°.
31. Relation véritable de la mort de Charles 1, 8°.
 5. Historia della Grande Bretagna dal Leti. 1060, A. C.–1649, 5 v 12°.
32. Ld Clarendon's history of the rebellion, 1625–1660, 6 v. 8°.
33. Ludlow's Mémoirs, 1626–1672, 3 v. 8°.—
95. Temple's works 1665–1679, 2 v fol.
96. Account of the Rye house plot, 1683. fol.
34. Rochester's relation of a forgery, 8°.

Wynne's life of Jenkins–1685, 2 v fol.

35. Fox's history of James II, 8°.

6. Welwood's Memoirs, 1603–1689, 12°.

67. Histoire d'Angleterre de Rapin, 59 A. C.–1689, 10 v. 4°.

36. Hume's history of England, 59 A. C.–1688. 8 v. 8°.

7. Révolutions d'Angleterre, par le père d'Orléans, 59 A. C.–1691. 3 v 12°.

68. Dalrymple's memoirs of Gr. Britain and Ireland, 1681–1692, 4°

37. Birch's life of Tillotson, 1629–1694. 8°.

69. D'Auvergne's history of the campaign in Flanders of 1695, 4°.

97. Kennet's historians of England, to wit. Milton, Daniel, anonymus, Habington, Moore, Buck, L. Bacon, L. Herbert of Cherbury, Bp. of Hereford, Cambden, Wilson, 1060 A. C.–1702, 3 v fol.

98. Guthrie's history of England, and the continuation, 45. A. C.–1702, 2 v fol.

38. Political State for 1714, 7th vol. 8°.

39. Boyer's annals of Q. Anne, 1702–1714, 11 v 8°.

8. Home's chronological abridgment of the history of England, to 1714 12°.

99. Bishop Burnets history of his own times, 1643–1715, 2 v fol.

9. History of the duke of Marlborough, 1650–1722, 12°

40. Campbells lives of the admirals, 1060 A. C.–1727, 4 v 8°.

41. Historical register from 1714–1732, 18 v 8°.

100. Lediards Naval history of England. 1066–1734, 2 v fol.

42. Abrégé chronologique de l'histoire d'Angleterre, par Salmon, 53 A. C. 1741, 2 v 8°.

70. Mrs Macaulay's history of England, 1603–1742, 9 v 4°.

10. Ayre's life of Pope, 1688–1744, 2 v 12°.

11. Orrery's life of Swift, 1677–1745, 12°.

43. Chamberlayne's present state of Gr. Britain, 1755, 8°.

12. Histoire de la puissance navale de l'Angleterre, 777–1762, 2 v 12°.

44. Entick's history of the late war of 1755, 1748–1763, 5 v 8°.

101. Memoirs of Thomas Hollis, 1720–1774, 2 v fol

45. Annual register for 1761 and 1778, 2 v 8°.

46. Anecdotes of the life of Ld Chatham, 1708–1778, 3 v 8°.

13. Ld Orrery's history of England, 55 A. C.–1793. 2 v 12°.

48. Belsham's memoirs of the Kings of the house of Brunswick Lunenburg 1714–1793, 3 v 8°.

47. Belsham's history of Gr. Britain from the revolution, 1689–1714, 2 v 8°.

49. Plowden's history of the British Empire, 1792, 1793. 8°.
71. Baxter's history of England, 1060 A. C.–1801, 4°.
72. Stephens's history of the wars which arose out of the French revolution, 2 v 4°.
50. Wilson's history of the British expedition to Egypt, 1800–1801. 8°.
51. Tracts of Br. Biography, viz. Anecdotes sur les personnages principaux et Semple, 8°.
52. Public characters, 1754–1801. 2 v 8°.
53. Goldsmith's crimes of Cabinets. 8°.
54. The book of Kings, 6 v 8°
55. Memoirs of Priestley, 1733–1804, 2 v 8°.
56. Cumberland's Memoirs, 1732–1805. 8°.
57. Historical Tracts, Jenner &c 8°.
102. Dugdales Baronage fol.
14. Philips grandeur of the Law, 12°.
58. The Laws of honor, 8°.
15. The arms of the Nobility of Gr. Britain and Ireland, 16.
16. Kimber's Peerage of England, 16.
17.   Scotland, 16.
18.   Ireland 16.
19. History of the Robin Hood Society, 12°.
20. Court calendar for 1768 12°
73. McPherson's antiquities of Scotland, 4°.
103. Buchanani opera, fol.
59. Buchanani historia, 8°.
21. Mémoires du Marquis de Montrose, 2 v. 12°.
104. Melvils Memoirs. fol.
60. Buchan's life and writings of Fletcher, 1653–1703. 8°.
74. Warner's history of Ireland, 4°.
75.   "   "   of the Irish rebellion, 4°.
61. Mc Nevin's pieces of Irish history, 8°.
62. Sampson's Memoirs, 8°.
63. Sampson's survey of Londonderry, 8°.

Chapter 4.
Modern History.
American.

Ante-Revolutionary. General—Particular
Post-Revolutionary. General—Particular.

12. Valer on the peopling of America, pamphlet 8°.
13. Holmes' American annals, 8° 1ˢᵗ & 2ᵈ vols
14. The American Library, p. 4°.
15. Histoire des deux Indes par l'abbé Raynal 11. v. 8°
16. Précis de l'histoire des deux Indes de Raynal, 8°.
 1. Burke's account of the European settlements in America, 2 v 12°.
17. Robertson's history of America, 1ˢᵗ and 3ᵈ vols, 8°
18.   ″   ″   ″   9ᵗʰ and 10ᵗʰ books, 8°
19. Oldmixon's British Empire in America, 2 v 8°.
21. Colden's history of the five nations, 8°.
20. Douglas' Summary of the British Settlements in America, 2 v 8°.

22. Washington's journal, 1753, 8°.
72. Bouquet's expedition, 4°.
23. Review of the Military operations in N. Am. 8°.
24. Mather's tracts relating to New England, p 4°.
73.   ″   Ecclesiastical history of New England, fol.
 2. Morton's New-England's Memorial 12°.
25. Belknap's history of New Hampshire, 3 v 8°.
26. Hutchinson's history of Massachusetts-bay. 2 v 8°.
27. Collection of papers relating to the history of Massachusetts, 8°.
28. Winthrop's journal, 1630–1644 8°.
29. William's Natural and civil history of Vermont, 8°.
30. Ethan Allen's vindication of Vermont against New York, 8°.
31. Smith's history of New York. 8°.
32. Smith's history of New Jersey. 8°

33. Historical Review of Pennsylvania, 8°.
34. Proud's history of Pennsylvania, 2 v 8°.
74. Smith's history of Virginia, p fol.
75. Keith's History of Virginia, 4°.

3. Histoire de la Virginie, par Beverley, 12°.
35. An Account of Bacon's rebellion in a letter from T. M. to Ld Oxford. 8°. M.S.
36. Stith's history of Virginia, 8°.
37. Burke's history of Virginia, 3 v 8°.
38. Hewitt's history of S. C. 2^d vol. 8°.
4. Phelps' Memoirs, 12°.
5. The history of Barbadoes, 12°.—
39. Concise historical account of the British Colonies in N. America, 8°.
40. History of the present war (1775) 2^d v 8°.
76. Histoire de la dernière guerre (1775) 4°.
6. Histoire de la dernière guerre (1775–1783) 3 v 12°.
41. Andrews' history of the American war, 4 v 8°.
42. Gordon's history of the independence of the U.S. of America, 4 v 8°.
43. Mrs Warren's history of the American revolution, 3 v 8°.
44. Ramsays history of the American revolution, 2 v 8°.
45. Révolution de l'Amérique par rapport à la Caroline Meridionale. par Ramsay, 2 v 8°.
46. Ramsay's history of the revolution of S Carolina, 2 v 8°.
47. Storia della guerra dell'Independenza degli S. U. d'America, dal Botta, 4 v 8°.
48. Histoire de l'administration du Ld North, par d'Auberteuil, 8°.
49. Essais historiques sur les anglo-Américains, par d'Auberteuil, 2. v. 8°.
50. Histoire des troubles de l'Amérique par Soulès, 4 v 8°.
51. Histoire de la révolution de l'Amérique Septentrionale, par Chas et Le Brun, 8°.
7. Deane's intercepted Letters, 12°.
52. Burgogne's State of his expedition from Canada 8°.
53. Narrative of Clinton's & Cornwallis' conduct in America, 8°
77. Tarletons history of the Campaign of 1781, 1781. 4°.
54. Mc Kensie's Strictures on Tarleton's history, 8°.
55. Heath's Memoirs 8°.

56. Memoirs of Genl. Charles Lee, 8°.
57. Henry Lee's Memoirs of the war in the Southern department of the U.S. 2 v 8°.
58. Moultrie's Memoirs of the American Revolution 2 v 8°
59. Le Spectateur Américain, par Mandrillon, 8°
60. Cary's American State papers, (Gen. Washington's letters) 2 v 8°.
61. Washington's life by Marshall, 5 v 8°.
 8. Washington's life, with anecdotes, by Weems, 12°.
62. Ramsay's life of Washington, 8°.
63. Jay and Littlepage's letters p. 4°.
64. The American and British Chronicle from 1773 to 1783, 8°.
65. Tracts in Biography, viz. Franklin, Bowdoin, M[c] Pherson, Cullen, 8°.
78. Tracts in American history, viz. Jennings and Lawrence, Jay and Littlepage, Jones and Landais, Vergennes, 4°.

66. Pamphlets historical 8°.
 9. Historical account of the Wallabout, 12°.
67. Minot's history of the insurrection in Massachusetts, in 1786. 8°.
68. Findlay's history of the insurrection in Pennsylvania, in 1794. 8°.
69. Breckenridge's incidents of the insurrection in Pennsylvania, 8°.
10. The treaty of 1794, between Gr. Br. and the U.S. with documents and Strictures, by M Carey. 12°.
70. Wood's history of the administration of John Adams, 8°.
11. Clarke's Naval history of the U.S. 2 v 12°.
71. Barton's Memoirs of Rittenhouse, 8°.

Newspapers.

88.	Virginia Gazettes	from 1741 to 1783, 12 v vol and 1 v 4°.
81.	Massachusetts papers.	1797—1807, 9 vols
83.	New York. d°	1789—1807. 13.
85.	Philadelphia	1786—1800. 35.
79.	Bache & Aurora	1795—1813. 19.
90.	Universal Gazette.	1798—1807. 7.
84.	National Intelligencer,	1801—1813. 12.
80.	Baltimore papers.	1799—1800. 2.
82.	Miscellaneous Gazettes,	1795—1813. 18.

89. Virginia   d°   1795—1813. 18.
87. Raleigh   d°   1800.
86. Ph. prices cur.   1802.—1807, 1.

Chapter. 5.

History—Ecclesiastical.

 1. Histoire des Oracles de Fontenelle, 16
17. Nicephori Callisti Ecclesiasticæ historiæ, Gr. Lat. Langi, Lut. Par. 1630
    2 v fol.
18. Eusebii Ecclesiastica historia, Gr. Lat. Valesii, fol.
19. Socratis et Sozomeni historia ecclesiastica, Gr. Lat. Valesii, fol.
20. Theodoretus, Evagrius, Philostorgius, et Theodorus, Gr. Lat. Valesii, fol.
 2. Histoire de l'Eglise d'Eusebe, Socrate, Sozomene, Theodoret, Evagre,
    Photius, et Nicephore Calliste, par Coussin, 6 v 12°.
 3. Sulpicius Severus, Elzevir, 16
21. Historia Consilii Florentini Sguropuli, Gr. Lat. Secundi, fol Hagaecomites,
    1660.
10. Fra. Paolo, Istoria del consilio Tridentino, 2 v p 4°.
22. History of the council of Trent by Pietro Suave Politano (i.e. Paolo Sarpi
    Vineto) Eng. by Brent, fol
 4. Vita del Padre Paolo, del Criselini, 12°.
15. Platina, Onuphrius et Cicarella de Vitiis Pontificum, 4°.
16. Bower's lives of the Popes, 2 v 4°.
 5. Vita di Sista V da Leti, 3 v. 12°.
 6. Histoire des Croisades par Maimbourg, 4 v 16.
 7. History of Monastical conventions, 12°.
 8. Vertot, origine de la grandeur de la cour de Rome, 12°
 9. Abrégé chronologique de l'histoire ecclesiastique, 3 v 12°.
11. Mosheim's Ecclesiastical history, 6 v 8°.
12. Stackhouse's history of the bible, 5 v 8°.

34

13. Spelman's history of Sacrilege, 8°.
14. Bede's history of the Church of Eng. translated by Stapleton, p 4°.
23. Anglia Sacra Whartoni, 2 v fol.
24. Burnet's history of the reformation, 3 v fol.
25. History of the reformation in Scotland, fol.

Chapter 6.

History—Natural. Physics. Natural Philosophy.

1. Clerici Physica, 12°.
2. Physique de Rohault, 2 v 16.
3. Spectacle de la Nature de la Pluche, 11 v 12°.
24. Franklin's philosophical works, 4°.
    (Franklin's works electrical, physical and meteorological, 4°) in his works.
    (Franklin on electricity, 4°) in his works.
7. Description of Nairn's Electrical Machine, 8°.
4. a. Baconi historia Naturalis ventorum, 16.
8. Williams' thermometrical Navigation, 8°.
25. Tracts in Cosmology, 4° viz. Pownal, Williams, Parmentier, Planaza, Ingenhoutz. Barton
9. Tracts in Cosmology, geology, mineralogy, botany &ᶜ viz Peyrouse, Churchman Mitchel, Rouelle, McLurg, Bland, Rush, p 4°.
10. Tracts in Physics, viz. Jones, Rush, Barton, Megatherium, Peale, Mitchel, Devese, Davis, 8°.
26. Tracts in Physics, viz, Delambre, Ginguené, Rampasse, Delile, Conover, Humbolt, Pearson, Giradin, De Fer, Lambert, Davy, Sinclair, Gallatin, 4°.
11. Lithologie Atmospherique, par Isarn 8°.
12. Kirwan's temperature of different Latitudes, 8°.
13. Idées sur la Météorologie, par De Luc, 8°

4. b. Météorologie des Cultivateurs, 12°
5. Annuaire Météorologique, par Lamarck, 12°.
27. Météorologie de Marseilles, 1779—1786, 4° M. S.
28. Ephemerides Meterologicae Palatinæ, 1781—5, 5 v 4°.
14. Ephemerides Mediolanenses anni 1779. 8°.
29. Ellicot's Astronomical and thermometrical observations on the Mississippi, 4°.
15. Histoire Naturelle des Volcans, par Ordinaire, 8°.
16. Hamilton's, Sir W^m. observations on Vesuvius & Ætna, 8°.
17. L'action du feu central, par Rome de l'Isle, et lettre sur la chaleur du globe, par M. L. S. 8[°]
18. De Luc sur les Montagnes, l'histoire de la Terre et de l'homme, 5 v 8°.
19. De Luc sur la Suisse et le climat d'Hieres, Vol 1. part. 1ère 8°
20. Géologie de Faujas de St Fond. 1st v 8°.
30. Géologiques de Faujas de St Fond, 4°.
21. Essai de Géologie, par Faujas de St Fond, 8°
31. Histoire Naturelle de la Montagne de St Pierre, de Faujas, 4°
22. Recueil de dissertations, par La Sauvagère, 8°.
6. Tableaux de la Nature, par Humbolt, 2 v 12°.
23. Archaeologiae Philosophical, Burnet, p 4°.
32. Burnet's Theory of the Earth. fol.
33. Woodward, histoire naturelle de la Terre, 4°.
34. Epoques de la Nature, de Buffon, 4°.
35. Whitehurst on the formation of the Earth, 4°.

Chapter 7th

Agriculture—

1. Cato, Varro, Columella et Palladius de re rustica, p 8°.
19. Economie rurale de Saboureux (Sc. Cato, Varro, Columella, Palladius et Vegetius) 6 v [8°]
20. Dickson's husbandry of the antients, 2 v 8°.
21. The country Farmer (Maison rustique) p 4°

22. Mortimer's husbandry, 2 v 8°.
23. Bradley's husbandry, 3 v 8°.

63. Bradley's experimental husbandry 4°.
24. Bradley on the four elements 8°.
 2. Jacob's country gentleman's vade mecum 12°.
25. Hale's body of husbandry, 4 v 8°
64. Théatre d'Agriculture de De Serres, 2 v 4°.

65. Duhamel's husbandry, 4°.
 3. L'Agricoltore del Frinci, 2 v 12°.
26. Réflexions sur l'agriculture de Naples, par Tupputi 8°.
 4. Dizzionario d'Agricoltura dal Ranconi, 2 v 8° p.
72. Evelyn's Terra, by Hunter, g 4°.
27. Home's principles of agriculture and vegetation, 8°.
28. Fordyce's Agriculture, 8°.
 5. Mills' chemical Elements of Agriculture, 12°.
29. Hale's Statical Essays, 2 v 8°.
30. Home's gentleman farmer, 8°.
31. Young's rural economy, 3 v 8°.
32. a.   ″   travels, 2 v 8°
32. b.   ″   Farmer's guide, 2 v 8°.

33. Spurrier's practical farmer, 8°.
34. Parkinson's experienced Farmer, 2 v 8°.
 6. Corso di Agricultura dal Proposito Lastri, 5 v 12°.
35. Istruzzione elementari di agricoltura del Fabbroni, 8°.
36. Recherches sur les végétaux nourissans, par Parmentier 8°.
39. Mémoires d'agriculture de Silvestre &ᶜ, 8°.
40. La Charrue, 8°
66. Voyages Agronomiques de Neufchateau, 4°.
41. Pratique de l'Agriculture, par Drouette Richardot, 8°.
42. Boardley's Sketches on rotation of crops, 8°
43.   ″   Essays and notes on husbandry, 8°
44. Peters' agricultural enquiries on Gypsum, 8°.
 7. Taylor's Arator, or Agricultural Essays, 12°.
45. Memoirs of the Philadelphia Society of Agriculture, 2 v 8°.

45. a.—45 b. D°, 3 v.
67. Transactions of the Agricultural Society of New York. 4°.
46. Statistical reports, 8°.
68. Agricultural reports, 3 v 4°.
8. Duhamel sur la conservation des grains, 12°.
9. Duhamel et Tillet, histoire de l'insect qui dévore les grains de l'angoumois, 12°.
69. Ginanni del Malattie del grano in erbe, 4°
73. Proceedings of the British privy council, on the insect called the Hessian fly, fol.
47. a. Tracts in Agriculture, to wit. Fowler, Bordley, Kirwan Logan, 8°.
47. b. Pamphlets in Agriculture, 8°, to wit. Strickland, Moore, Boardley, Logan, Tessier, Sinclair.
48. Agricultural pamphlets, 8°.
49. Pamphlets on Agriculture, 8°.
10. Tracts in Agriculture, 8°, to wit, Fabbroni, Parmentier, Maupin.
11. Traite de la vigne de Bidet et Duhamel, 2 v 12°.
50. Maupin sur la vigne, 8°
51. Traité sur la vigne, par Chaptal, Rozier, Parmentier, et Dussieux 2 v 8°.
52. Della coltivazione degli Ulivi del Vettori é degli Agrumi, 8°.
53. Lateyrie du cotonnier et de sa culture, 8°
74. Evelyn's sylva, fol.
54. Daubenton's advice to Shepherds, 8°
55. Lasteyrie sur les bêtes à laine d'Espagne, 8°.
56. Livingston's Essay on sheep. 8°.
57. Bakewell on the influence of soil and climate on wool, 8°.
75. Millar's gardener's dictionary, fol.
70. Dictionnaire des jardiniers de Millar, par Chazelles, 5 v 4°.
58. Millar's gardener's chronicle, 8°.
59. Bradley's gardening, 8°
12. Abercrombie's gardener's pocket dictionary, 3 v 12°.
13. Every man his own gardener, by Mawe, 12°.

14. Le jardinier solitaire, 12°
71. Le parfait jardinier, par Mallet, 4°
15. American gardener, by Gardiner and Hepburn, 2 v 12°.
60. Mc Mahon's american gardener's Calendar, 8°.

16. A treatise on gardening by John Randolph, 16.
17. Culture de la grosse asperge de Hollande, par Filassier 12°.
18. De la Brosse, de la culture du Figuier, 12°.
76. Langley's Pomona, fol.
61. Forsyth on the culture and management of fruit trees, 8°
62. Traité sur les abeilles, par della Rocca, 3 v 8°.

Chapter 8.

Chemistry.

30. Neumann's chemistry, by Lewis 4°.
 7. Mᶜ Queer's chemistry, 2 v 8°.
 1. Dictionnaire de Chimie de Macquers, 4 v 12°.
 8. Chimie de Beaumé, 3 v 8°.
 2. Watson's chemistry, 5 v 12°.
 3. Mémoires de Chimie de Scheele, 12°.
 4. Scheele, de l'air et du feu, 12°.
 9. Dobson's commentary on fixed air, 8°.
10. Rouland, de l'air, 8°.
11. Sigaud de la Fond sur l'air 8°.
12. Dela Méthérie sur les différentes espèces d'air, 8°.
13. Crawford on animal heat, 8°.
14. Ingenhousz, expériences sur les végétaux, 2v 2ᵈ. 8°.
15. Ingenhousz, expériences physiques, 2 v 8°.
16. Cramer on Metals, 8°.
17. Pennington's economical and chemical essays, 8°.
18. Traité élémentaire de chimie de Lavoisier, 2 v 8°.
19. Elémens d'histoire Naturelle et de Chimie de Fourcroy, 4 v 8°.
20. Elémens de Chimie de Chaptal, 3 v 8°
 5. Conversations on Chemistry, 2 v 12°.
21. Leçons élémentaires de Chimie, par Adet, 8°.
22. Ewell's discourses on Modern Chemistry, 8°.

23. Morveau, des Moyens de désinfecter l'air, 8°.
24. Foronda, Lecciones de Chemica, 8°.
25. Smith's oration or sketch of the revolutions in Chemistry, 8°.
 6. Jacob's chemical pocket companion, 12°.
26. Jacob's experiments on Urinary and Intestinal Calculi, 8°.
27. Chemistry tracts, 8°.
28. Cooper's introductory lecture in Chemistry, 8°.
29. Cazalet Théorie de la Nature, 8°.

Chapter 9.

Surgery.

1. Waters' abridgment of Benjamin Bell's Surgery, 8°.
2. Smiths abridgment of John Bell's principles of Surgery, 8°.
3. John's Bell's discourses on wounds, adhesion and amputation, 8°.
4. Cooper's first lines of the practise of Surgery, 8°.
7. Mauriceau, Maladies des Femmes Grosses, 4°.
5. Théorie et pratique de l'art du Dentiste, par Laforgue, 8°.
6. La-Forest, l'art de Soigner les pieds, 12°.

Chapter 10.

Medicine.

89. Dictionnaire des drogues Simples de Lemery, 4°.
15. Elémens de Pharmacie, par Beaume, 8°.
16. Quincey's Dispensatory, 8°.

1. Salmon's supplement to his dispensatory, p. 8°.
17. New Dispensatory, 8°.
2. Fuller's Pharmacopœia, 12°.
3. Pharmacopœia Londinensis, 12°.
18. London Dispensatory, by Healde, 8°.

19. Cullen's Materia Medica, 2 v 8°.
4. Tazewell's vade-mecum Medicum, 12°.
5. Pharmacopœia Massachusetts, 12°.
20. Blancardi Lexico Medicum, 8°.
21. Blancard's Physical Dictionary, 8°.
22. Quincey's Medicinal Dictionary, 8°.
98. Hippocratis opera, Gr. Lat. fol.
23. Hippocratis opera omnia, Gr. Lat. Vander Linden, 5 v 8°.
24. Celsus de re Medicâ, p 4°.
99. Aretaei opera, cum commentario Henischii, fol
25. Mercurialis, p 4°.
100. Gorraei definitiones Medicæ, Nicandri Theriaca et Alexipharmaca, Hippocrates de Genitura, Natura pueri, Jusjurandum, de arte, antiqua Medecina et de Medico, fol.
101. Riverius' practice of physic, fol.
6. Boerhaave, Institutio Medicinæ, 12°.
26. Shaw's practice of physic, 2 v 8°.
27. Brooke's introduction to physic, 8°.
28. Brooke's practice of physic, 8°.
7. Ouvrages de Tissot, 16 v 12°.
29. Tissot's advice, 8°.
30. Buchan's Domestic Medicine, 8°.
31. Compendium of Physic and Surgery, g 12°.
32. Cullen's practice of physic, 4 v. 8°
33. Darwin's Zoonomia, 3 v 8°.
8. Brown's elements of Medicine, 12°.
34. Barnwell's physical investigations, 8°.
35. Ewell's medical companion, 8°.
36. Certitude de la Médecine, et autres écrits de Cabanis, 8°.
37. Coup d'oeil sur les révolutions et sur la réforme de la Médecine, par Cabanis 8°.

90. Millar on the change of opinion in religion, politics, medicine, 2 v 4°.
38. Aphorisms of Sanctorius by Quincey, 8°
 9. Boerhaave aphorismi, 12°.
39. Harvei opera, 2 v p 4°.
91. Sydenhami opera, 4°.
40. Sydenham's works, 8°
41. Meade's Medical works, 8°.
42. Strother's causes and cures, 8°.
10. Dovar's Physician's legacy, 12°.
43. Astruc's Diseases of children, 8°.
44. Pitcairn's works, 8°.
45. De la Méthode Jatroliptice, par Chrestien, 8°.
46. The family companion for Health, 8°.
47. Tableau des variétés de la vie humaine, par Daignan, 2 v 8°.
48. Adair's Medical cautions to invalids, 8°.
49. Adairs natural history of the body and mind 8°.
50. Peale on the means of preserving health. 8°.
11. Ricketson's means of preserving health, 12°.
51. Cutbush on the health of Soldiers and Sailors, 8°
52. Trattati Fisici del Cocchi, p 4°.
53. Wainewright's non-naturals, 8°.
54. Short on Tea, 8°.
92. Fontana Sur les poisons 4°.
55. Baynard on cold bathing, 8°.
56. Macbride's experimental essays, 8°.
57. Maclurg on the bile, 8°.
58. Valentin de la fièvre jaune, 8°.
59. Berthe, de la maladie (fièvre jaune) d'andalousie de 1800, 8°.
60. Facts on the pestilential fever of Philadelphia, by the College of Physicians, 8°.
61. Rush on yellow fever, 8°.
62. Tracts on the yellow fever, Palloni, Devere, Hardie, Anon, Blanc, Miller, 8°
63. Oniana, 8°.
93. Hunter on the venereal disease, 4°.
64. Turner on Gleets, 8°.
65. Tracts in Medicine, to wit, animal Magnetism & Syphilis, 8°.

94. Evidence at large on Jenner's discovery of vaccine inoculation, 4°.
95.
12. Aiken on the cow pox, 12°.
96. Tracts on the Cowpox, 4°.
66. Waterhouse on the kinepox, 8° (Catalogue N° 67)
67. Beddoe's observations on Calculus &ᶜ 8°.
68. Liger on the gout, 8°.
69. Warner on the gout, 8°.
70. Cadogan on the gout, 8°.
71. Falconer's observations on Cadogan, 8°.
72. Essay on the treatment of the gout, 8°.
97. Cullen's lecture on the gout, M. S. 4°.
73. Pfieffer's inaugural dissertation on the gout, 8°.
74. Mandeville on hysterics, 8°.

75. Medical observations, 2 v 8°.
76. Rush's medical enquiries, 2ᵈ & 4ᵗʰ vols. 8°.
77.   ″   Introductory lectures, 8°.
78. Fothergill on the Suspension of vital action, 8°.
79. Young's physiology, 8°.
80. Pamphlet, medical, 8°.
81. Tracts in medicine, 8°. animal magnetism, syphilis.
82. Tracts in medicine, 8°.

83. Maese's dissertation on the rabies, 8°.
84. Woodhouse's dissertation on the persimmon tree, 8°.
85. Rogers de Dysenteria, 8°.
86. Stokes de Asphyxia, 8°.
87. Shattuk's dissertations, 8°.
13. Braken's Traveller's pocket companion, 12°.
88. Gibson's Farmer's dispensatory, 8°.
14. Mason's pocket companion for the horse, 12°.

Chapter 11.

Natural-history—Animals
Anatomy.

 1. Lassus, histoire des découvertes en Anatomie, 8°
 2. L'Anatomie de Nogues, 12°.
 9. L'Homme et le Monde de Descartes, par De la Forge, 4°.
 3. Anatomia del Cocchi, p 4°.
 4. Cheselden's Anatomy, 8°.
10. Winslow's Anatomy, translated by Douglas, 4°.
 5. Anatomy of the human body, by John & James Bell, 4 v 8°.
11. Hunter's natural history of the human teeth, 4°.
 6. Leçons d'anatomie comparée, de Cuvier, 2 v 8°.
 7. Blumenbach's short system of comparative anatomy, by Lawrence, 8°.
 8. Ball's analytical view of the animal economy, 12°.

Chapter 12.

Natural-history—Animals
Zoology.

 1. A philosophical survey of the animal creation, 12°.
30. Histoire des animaux d'Aristole, par Camus, Gr. Fr. 2 v 4°.
10. Plinicus Secundus Dalechampii, 6 v 8° Francoperti, 1608.
11. Plinii historia naturalis, Not. var. 3 v 8°.
31. Histoire Naturelle de Pline, Lat. Fr. 12 v 4°.
12. Linnaei Systema Naturae et Mantissa prior, editio 12°, 4 v 8°.
13. Linnaei Mantissa Altera. 8°

14. Linnaei Fauna Suecica. 8°

2. Histoire Naturelle de Buffon et Daubenton, 32 v 12°. Paris 1752.

3. Buffon, Supplément, 12. v ⎫
4.   ″ , Mineraux   9. ⎬   39 v 12°.
5   ″ , Oiseaux   18.⎭

6. Buffon, Continuation, 12 v 12°, wanting the 1ˢᵗ & 5ˢᵗ Des oiseaux.

32. Les oiseaux de Buffon, avec des planches enluminées, 10 v 4° (646 plates).

7. Cepede, histoire naturelle des Quadrupedes, ovipares, et des Serpens, 4 v 12°.

33.   ″ , histoire naturelle des poissons. 5 v 4°.

15. Abrégé du Système de la nature de Linnée, par Gilibert, 8°.

16. Manuel d'histoire naturelle, par Blumenbach, 2 v 8°.

17. Tableau élémentaire de l'histoire naturelle des animaux, par Cuvier, 8°.

8. a. Dictionnaire d'histoire Naturelle de Bomare, 9 v 12°.

8. b. Burkhard's elements of the philosophy of nature, by Smith, 12°.

18. Goldsmith's animated Nautre, 4 v 8°.

19. Histoire naturelle du genre humain par Virey, 2 v 8°.

20. Smith on the variety in the human Species, 8°.

9. Uncertainty of the signs of Death, 12°.

21. Traité des Monstres, de Palfyn, p. 4°.

34. Tyson's ourang-outang. p. fol.

35. Penant's history of quadrupeds, 2 v 4°.

42. Pisoni Medicina Brasiliensis ⎫
                                   ⎬ De Laet. fol.
     ″   Maregravii historia naturalis Brasiliae ⎭

22. Zoologie géographique, par Zimmerman, 8°

C. Catesby's Natural history of Carolina, 2 v g fol.

43. Wilson's American ornithology, fol. 8 v bound in 7.

44. Willoughby's ornithology, fol.

45. Barton's fragments of the Natural history of Pennsylvania, fol. pamphlet.

36. Insectorum Theatrum Wottoni, Gesneri, Pennii, Moufeti, p. fol.

23. Oeuvres Physiques de Bonnet, 12 v 8°.

37. Experienze intorno a diverse cose naturali del Redi, 4°.

24. Vipere e Anguillette del Fontana, 8°.

25. Fisica Animale è vegetabile del Spallanzani, 4 v 8°

26. Adams on the Microscope, 8°.
27. Baker's Microscope. 8°
28. Baker's natural history of the Polypus. 8°.
38. Ellis' Zoophytes, 4°.
39. Barrington's Miscellanies, 4°.
40. Tracts in Zoology, to wit,—Camus & Spållanzani, 4°
29. Zoological tracts, 8°.
41. Tableau des Arénaides, par Walkenaer, g. 8°

Chapter 13.
Natural-history.
Botany.

 1. Dioscorides, Gr. Lat. p. 8°.
32. Dioscoride, traduccione è discorsi del Matthioli, fol. Ven. 1573.
33. Theophrasti Eresii historia plantarum, Gr. Lat. Gasae, Commentariis Bo-daei à Stapel, Jul. Caes. Scaligeri et Constantini, fol Amst. 1644.
34. Parkinson's herbal. fol.
 2. Boerhaave's Historia plantarum, 12°.
29. Tournefort Institutiones rei herbariae, 2 v 4°.
 4. Linnaeus on the sexes of plants, and study of nature by Smith, 8°
 5. Linnaei Philosophia botanica, 8°.
 6.   ″   Genera Plantarum, 8° 6th Ed.
 7.   ″   Species plantarum, 2 v 8°, 2d Ed.
 8.   ″   Critica Botanica, 8°
 9.   ″   Fundamenta Botanica, Edente Gilibert, 3 v 8°.
10.   ″   Flora Lapponica, 8°
11. Linnaeus system of vegetables, Litchfields translation, 8°.
12. Le Botannister cultivateur, par Dumont-Courset, 4 v 8°.
13. Darwin's Botanic Garden, 8°.
 3. Synopsis plantarum, Persoon, 2 v 12°.

30. Clayton's Flora Virginica, 4°.
14. Crownenshield's hortus siccus, 8°. M. S.
15. Flora Carolineana Walteri, 8°.
16. Sheecut's Flora Caroliniensis, 8°.
17. Catalogus plantarum Americæ Septentrionalis, Henrici Muhlenberg. 8°.
18. Flora Boreali-Americana, Michaux, 2 v 8°.
35. Les chênes d'Amérique, par Michaux, fol.
31. Histoire des Arbres forestieres de l'Amerique Septentrionale, par Michaux,
19. Marshal's American grove, 8°.
20. Bradley's Botanical Dictionary, 2 v 8°.
21. Rousseau's botany by Martyn, 8°.
22. Barton's Elements of Botany, 8°.
23. Waterhouse's Botanist, 8°.
24. Nomenclator Botanicus, Lat. Ang. Gal. Germ. Suec. Dan. 8°.
25. Manuel des végétaux par St Germain, 8°.
26. Tracts in Botany, Marshal, Gouan, Kennedy and Lee, 8°.

27. Roscoe's address on opening the Botanic Garden of Liverpool, 8°.
28. Catalogue of the Botanic garden at Liverpool, 8°.

Chapter 14.

Natural history.
Mineralogy.

1. Cronstadt's Mineralogy, by Magellon, 2 v 8°.
2. Minéralogie de Haüy, 5 v 8°.
3. Da Costa's elements of Conchology, 8°.
5. Short's history of Mineral waters, 2 v 4°.
4. Recueil sur les Salines, par Struve, 12°.

Chapter 15.

History—Natural. Occupations of Man. Technical Arts.

29. The handmaid to the arts, 2 v 8°.
 1. Bibliothéque Physico-économique, 14 v. 12°, 1782—1790.
30. Journal Polytype pour l'année 1786. 9 v 8°.
 2. Locke on education, 12°.
92. Essai général d'Education, par Jullien, 4°.
31. Eudoxe, entretiens sur l'etude, par Deleuse, 2 v 8°.

 3. La civilité puérile, 12° Troyes, chez Garnier.
32. Méthode élémentaire de Pestolozzi, par Chavannes, 8°.
 4. Neef's plan of Education, 12°.
33. Lancaster's improvements in Education. 8°
34. Knox on Education, 8°.
 5. Chesterfield's letters, 4 v 12°.
35. The preceptor, v. 2ᵈ. 8°
 6. Fisher's young man's companion, 12°.

36. Tracts in the arts, to wit, Quisnay, Voyages, Scott. 8°.
37. Mémoire sur l'académie de Richmond, par Quisnay, 8°.
 7. Manière d'instruire les sourds et Muets, par l'Espine, 12°.
38. Green on the speech of the deaf & dumb, 8°.
39. Cadmus or on the elements of written language, by Thornton, 8°.
40. Rice's art of reading, 8°.
41. Miss Crownenshield's specimens of Penmanship, 8°. M. S.
42. Pelham's system of notation, 8°.
 8. Shelton's Tachygraphy, 12°
43. Weston's short hand, 8°.
44. Tracts in the arts, short hand, copying machine, Blanchard, Dance, 8°.
93. Calson's specimens of printing types, pamp. 4°.
45. Histoire de la stéréotype, par Camus, 8°.
102. Perkins' bank bill test, pamphlet.

46. Gordon's counting house, 8°.
47. Haye's modern bookkeeping, 8°.
48. Cavallo's history of Aerostation, 8°.

49. Tracts on Navigation, to wit, Naval Architecture, Rumsey, D'Arnal, Canals, Payrouse, Barnes, 8°.

50. Canals, to wit, Gallatin's report, Smith, Colles, Tatham, 8°.
51. Tracts on wet Docks, Quays & Warehouses for London, 8°
94. Vocabulaire de Marine, par L'Escalier, 3 v 4°.
52. Clarke's Vegecius, 8°.
 9. a. Arte della guerra de Machiavelli, 12°.
 9. b. Sr Walter Raleigh's Essays, 12°.
95. L'Ecole de Mars par Guignard, 2 v 4°.
53. Saxe's Reveries, 8°.
96. De Rohan, Abrégé des guerres de Gaule, 4°.
10. Mémoires historiques et militaires de Feuquières, 2 v 12°.
11. Mémoires de Feuquières, 1st, 3^d, 4th vols. 12°.
12. Mémoires de Montécuculi, 12°.
97. Histoire de la Milice Française, 2 v 4°.
54. Digge's Stratisticos, 8°.
55. Bland's military discipline, 8°.
56. Fisher's Military tactics, 8°.
57. The Army & Navy of Gr. Br. 8°
58. Rules for the government of an army, 8°
59. Duane's hand book for Infantry, 8°.
60. Duane's American Military Library, 8°.
98. Fulton's Torpedo War, pamphlet, 4°.
61. }
99. } Tousard's American Artillerist's companion, 8° and 4°.
62. }
103. } Scheel's treatise on Artillary, 8° and fol.

63. Kosciusko's Manœuvres of horse artillery, 8°.
64. Military tracts, 8°. to wit. Shee, Godefroi, Truxtun.

13. Adye's bombardier and pocket Gunner, 12°.
65. Military and political hints, by De la Croix, 8°.
14. Blackwell's art of defence, 12°.
66. Rei accipitrariæ Scriptores, et de Cura Canum, Demetrius, Symmachus, Theodotion, Thuanus, et Fracastorius, Gr. Lat. Catalan, p 4°. Lutetial, 1612.
15. Le jeu des échecs, de Giacomo Greco, 16.

67. Lambe's history of Chess, and Philidor, analyse des Echecs, 8°.
16. Traité des Echecs du Caffe de Foy, 12°.
17. Hoyle's games, 12°.
68. Amusemens physiques de Pinetti, 8°.
69. La Faye, sur la chaux des Romains, 8°.
70. Rumford's Essays, 2 v 8°.
71. L'architecture rurale de Cointeraux, 8°.
72. Rural Economy, by Johnson, 8°
73. Theatrum Machinarum universale, 1 v 8°, and 1 v. g fol. D
74. Evans' Millwright and Miller, 8°.
75. The builder's price book
104. L'art de tourner, par Plumier, fol.
18. L'art de conduire les pendules, par Berthoud, 16
19. L'art des expériences, par l'abbé Nollet, 3 v 12°.

76. Tracts on steam engines, by Rumsey & Fitch, the Seine 8°.
105. Komarzewski's Theodolite, pam. fol.
77. Arts, Tracts, inventors Dorsey, Lippi, Polymathique, Bridge, Guest, Cutting, Montgolfier's bélier hidraul., Boaz, Useful Cabinet, Dynamometer, 8°.
100. Tracts in the arts, Aerostatiques, Bird, Whitehurst, Education, Maupin, 4°
78. Treatise of husbandry, spinning, weaving &c. 8°
20. Truths on Manufactures, 12°.
79. Elémens de l'art de la teinture, par Berthollet, 2 v 8°.
80. Art de faire le vin, par Cossigny, 8°.
21. Fabbroni dell' arte di fare il vino, 12°.
81. Pamphlets in the arts, 8°.
22. Knight on the apple and pear, Cider & Perry, 12°.
82. The London and Country Brewer, 8°.
83. Combrun's theory and practice of brewing, 8°.

84. Richardsons philosophical principles of brewing, 8°.

85. Krafft's american distiller, 8°.
23. Apicius Coelius de opsoniis et condimentis, sive arte coquinariâ, 12° apud Waestburgios

24. Avis au peuple sur leur premier besoin, (le pain) par l'abbé Baudau, 12°.
25. Avis sur la manière de faire le pain, par Parmentier, 12°.
86. Le parfait boulanger, par Parmentier, 8°

26. Parmentier sur les pommes de terre, 12°.
27. Eale's Cookery, 12°.
28. Dictionnaire Domestique, 3 v 12°.

87. Tracts on potash and maple sugar. Williamos, Hopkins, remarks on Maple sugar, 8°.
88. Résultats de la Fabrication des sirops et des conserves de raisins, par Parmentier, 8°.
89. Fennel's plan of Salt works, 8°.
90. Fabrication de la poudre à cannon, par Cossigny, 8°.
91. Supplément sur la fabrication de la poudre à cannon, par Cossigny, 8°.
101. Manner of Making tar in Sweden, pam. 4°.

II   Philosophy.

Chapter 16.
Moral. Ethics.
1. Moral Philosophy.
2. Law of Nature and Nations.

  1. Hieroclis commentarius in aureâ Pythagoreorum carmina, Gr. Lat. 12°.
68. Aeschinis Dialogi, Gr. Lat. 8°.
  2. Xenophontis Memorabilia, Gr. Foulis, Eng. by Fielding, 2 v 12°.
136. Platonis opera Gr. Lat. Serrani, 3 v fol.
69. Plato. Gr. Stephani, et Lat. Ficini, 12 v 8°.
  3. Plato abridged by Dacier, Eng 2 v 12°.
  4. Aristotelus Ethica, Gr. Lat. Magiri, 12°.
  5. Theophrasti Caracteres, Gr. Lat. 12°. Foul.
  6. Epictetus, Cebes, Theophrastus, dialogues de Exilio, et Prodicus. 16°.
70. Epicteti Manuel, Gr. Lat. p 4°.
  7. Epicteti Enchiridion, &c Cebetis tabula, Simplicii commentarius, et Arriani dissertationes, Gr. Lat. Wolfii, versione Anglica dominae Carter. 3 v 12°.
  8. Epictetus Gr. Lat. Foulis, 12°.
137. Plotina opera philosophica, Gr. Lat. Ficini fol.
  9. Catonis distica. Sterling, 12°.
    (Cicero de officius) in op.
10. Id.   12°.
11. Id.   Eng. by Cockman, 12°.
    Cicero de Divinatione et de Fato ⎫
      ″   De Natura Deorum   ⎬   in op.
      ″   De Finibus bonorum   ⎭
12.   ″   De Finibus bonorum, Gronovii 12°.
      ″   Academica, in op.

71.   "   De Finibus et Academica, Eng. by Guthrie, 8°.
        "   (Tusculanæ disputationes) in op.
13.   "   Tusculana. Foulis, 12°.
14.   "   De Senectute et Somnium Scipionis, Lat. Gr. Theodori, 12°.
72.   "   Id. Eng. by Franklin with notes 8°.
15. D'olivet's thoughts of Cicero, Lat. Eng. 12°.
73. L. Annaei Senecae opera. Lat. Biponte et Fr. par La Grange, 10 v 8°.
138.   "   "   "   Eng. by Lodge, fol.
74. L. Annaei Senecae, et P. Syri Mimi Sententiae, not. Gruteri et vers. Graeca
     Scaligeri, 8°.
16. Adagiorum Erasmi Epitome. 24.
17. Plutarcha Moralia, Gr. Lat. 8. v. p 8°.
130. Plutarcha varia, Gr. Lat. Cruseri. 4 v p fol.
75. Demetrius Cydonius de Contemnendâ Morte, Gr. Lat. 8°.
18. Marci Antonini Commentarii ad Seipsum, Gr. Lat. 12°. Foul.
19. Marci Antonini corum quæ ad Seipsum, lib XII, Gr. Lat. Eng. 2 v 12°.
20. Maximi Tyrii dissertationes, Gr. Lat. 16. Oxon 1677.
76. Dissertations de Maximi de Tyr, par Combes Dounous, 2 v 8°.
21. Alexander Aphrodisiensis de Fato. Gr. Lat. 12°.
22. Minuti Felicis Octavius, 12°. Foulis
139. Phylostratus concerning the life of Apollonius the Tyanean, by Blount. fol.
77. Les causes premières, Sc. Ocellus Lucanus, Timaeus Locrus, et Aristoteles
     de Mundo, Gr. Fr. par l'abbé Batteuse, 2 v 8°.
23. Boetius de consolatione, 12°. Foulis.
78. Boece de Consolacion et de philosophie, translate par Johan de Meun
     p 4°.
79. Enfield's history of Philosophy, 2 v 8°.
24. Synopsis Metaphysicae, 12°.
80. Locke's Essay on the human understanding, 8°.
81. Bp. of Worcester's Answer to Locke's Essay, 8°.
82. Bolinbroke on innate principles, Fr. Eng. 8°.
83. Philosophie de Kant, par Villers, 8°.
84. Idéologie de Destutt Tracy, 3 v 8°.
131. Stewarts Elements of the philosophy of the Human Mind, 1ˢᵗ v 4°.
85. Enquiry into the nature of the Human Soul, 2 v 8°.
86. Appendix to the enquiry into the nature of the Soul, 8°.
87. Progrès de L'Espirt humain, par Condorcet, 8°.

25. Locke's conduct of the mind in the search after truth. 12°.
26. Malebranche de la recherche de la vérité, 2 v 12°.
27. Whitby's Ethics, p 8°.
28. Compendium Ethics, 12°.
29. De juramenti obligatione, Sanderson, 2 v 12°.
30. Puffendorf de officio hominis et civis, 12°.
88. Wollaston's religion of nature, 8°.
31. Hutchinson's Introduction to Moral Philosophy, 1st v 12°.
89. Hutchinson's ideas of Beauty & virtue, 8°.
90. Ld. Kaim's Natural religion, 8°.
32. Traité élémentaire de Morale et du Bonheur, 2 v in 18.
91. Price's Review of the principal questions in Morals, 8°.
92. Gros' Moral Philosophy, 8°.
33. Oeconomy of human life, 12°.

34. The rule of life, 12°
93. Harris' three treatises, 8°
35. Vanini de admirandis naturæ, reginæ deaeque mortalium arcanis, 12°.
36. Vanini amphitheatrum providentiæ, 12°
94. Spinosae tractatus theologico politicus, p 4°.
95. Spinosae opera posthuma, p 4°.
96. Spinosa's theological and political discourses, 8°
37. Œuvres philosophiques de Diderot, 3 v 12°.
    (Le Bon Sens, 12°, Diderot.) oeuvres

97. The System of Nature, Eng. 1st v 8°.
98. Œuvres d'Helvetius, 5 v 8° Ed. de Deuxponts, 1781.
99. Rapport du physique et du Moral de l'homme, par Cabanis, 2 v 8°.
132. Lettre de Trasibule à Leucippe, par Frerèt, 4° M. S.
38. Pensées sur la comète de 1680 par Bayle, 4 v 12°.
39. Bayle's philosophical commentary on Luke 14, 23, 2 v 12°.
100. Fable of the Bees 2d v 8°.
101. Ld Bolingbroke's philosophical works, 5 v 8°.
40. Massie's travels by Bayle, 12°.
41. Hume's Essays, 3d & 4t vols, 12°.
42. Recherches sur l'origine du despotisme oriental, par Boulanger, 12°.
133. Recherchs su lorigine del dispotismo orientale, del Boulanger, p. fol. M. S.

54

134. Christianesimo Svelato del Boulanger, tradotto dal Bellini. p fol. M. S.
 43. Philosophie de la Nature, par de Lisle, 3 v 12°.
102. Philosophie de l'Univers par Dupont, 8°
103. Ruines de Volney, 8°.
 44. Volney's ruins, 12°
104. De l'esprit des religions, par Bonneville, 2 v 8°.
105. Allen's Reason, the only oracle of man, 8°.
106. Peel's Truth & Reason, 8°
 45. Palmer's principles of Nature, 12°.
107. Tindal's christianity as old as the creation, 8°.
108. Chubb's tracts, 2 v 8°
 46. Dudgeon's philosophical works, 12°.
 47. History of the man after God's own heart, 12°.
 48. Blount's Miscellaneous works, 12°.
109. Voltaire's philosophical Dictionary, 8°.
110a.Voltaire philosophie de l'histoire, 8°.

 49. La certitude des preuves du Mahometisme, 12°.
 50. Traité des trois imposteurs, 12°.
111. Analyse de l'origine des Cultes, de Dupuis, par Tracey, 8°.
     (Priestley's Heath. Philos. compared with Revelation, 8° Chap. 17, N° 96)
 51. Locke on Toleration, 16.
     (Eloge de la Folie d'Erasme, par Guendiville, figures de Holbein, 12° post
     C. 36. N° 14)
 52. Essais de Montaigne, 3 v 12°, Bruxelles, 1659.
 53. Bacon's Essays, 12°.
 54. Maximes de la Rochefoucault, 12°.
 55. & 112. Caractères de la Bruyère, 1ˢᵗ v Eng 8° 2 v Fr. 12°.
113. Shaftesbury's characteristics, 3 v 8°.
114. Bréviaire des politiques, par de Salmozen, 8°.
115. Meilhan sur l'esprit et les moeurs. 8°.
116. Les Loisirs du Marquis d' Argenson, 2 v 8°.
 56. Lᵈ Kaim's art of thinking, 12°.
 57. Essai sur le caratère des Femmes par Thomas, 12°.
 58. Russels Essay on the character of Women, 12°.
 59. Gregory's Legacy to his daughters, 12°.
117. Lady Chudleigh's Essays, 8°.

60. Instructions for a young Nobleman, 12°.

61. Ochino on Polygamy 12°.

118. Sylva, or the Wood, by a Society, 8°.

119. Zimmerman de la Solitude, 8°.

120. Le Bonnet de Nuit de Mercier, 4 v 8°.

121. L'an 2440, de Mercier, 8°.

122. Lettres de Brutus, par Mércier, 8°.

123. Fraser's history of Man, 8°

124. Tracts in Ethics, to wit, Swedenburg, Castiglione, Mably, Lites forenses, état primitif, slave trade, Benezet, &c on Slavery, 8°.

62. Stewart's moral or intellectual Last will and testament, p fol 32.

125. Condorcet sur l'esclavage des Nègres. 8°.

63. Ramsay on African Slaves, 12°.

135. Tracts on slavery, to wit. Peyroux, Mifflin, Nesbitt, Abolition, clavière, 4°.

126. Tracts on Slavery, French. 8°.

64. Ray's horrors of slavery, 12°.

65. Branagan on the oppression of the exiled sons of Africa, 12°.

66. Branagan's Beauties of Philantrophy, 12°.

127. Grégoire de la Littérature des Nègres, 8°.

128. Grégoire on the faculties and literature of the Negroes, by Warden, 8°.

67. Clarkson's history of the abolition of the slave trade, in Gr. Br. 2 v 12°.

129. Caine's history of the convention of the Leeward Islands, 8°.

Ethics.

2. Law of Nature and Nations.

34. Beller's delineation of universal Law 4°.

18. Cumberland de legibus Naturæ, 4° p.

35. Cumberland on the Laws of Nature, 4°.

36. Burlamaqui Sur le Droit Naturel et Politique. 4°.

37.   ″   Principes du Droit politique, 4°.

19. Elémens de législation Nautrelle, par Perreau, 8°

20. Ward's Foundation and history of the Laws of Nations, 8°.

21. Grotius de Jure belli et pacis, 8°.
38. 〃 Droit de la Guerre, avec les notes de Barbeyrac, 2 v 4°.
39. Puffendorf, Droit des Gens, de Barbeyrac, 3 v 4°.
47. Id. Eng. Fol.
 1. Wolff, Droit de la Nature et des Gens, Lat. Fr. par Luzac, 6 v 12°.
40. Vattel, Droit des Gens, Ed. de 1775, 4°.
 2. 〃 〃 3 v 12°. Londres, 1758.
22. Droit des Gens Moderne, de L'Europe, par Martens, Eng. by Cobbett. 8°.
23. Institutions du droit de la Nature et des Gens, par Reyneval, 8°.
24. Synopsis Grotii, Clarkii et Lockii. 8°.
41. Code de l'humanité, par Felice, 13 v 4°.
 3. Vattel Questions de Droit Naturel, 12°.
 4. Recueil de Discours par Barbeyrac, 2 v 12°.
25. Lee's treatise of Captures in War, 8°.
    (Jenkinson's conduct of Gr. Br. as to Neutral Nations) in N° 33. post.
48. Selden's Mare clausum, fol.
 5. Id. Lat. 16.
 6. Préséance entr la France et L'Espagne, 12°.
26. El embaxador por D J A de vera y Cuniga, p 4°.
27. Bynkershock du Juga compétent des Ambassadeurs, avec les Notes de Bar-
    beyrac, 8°.
42. S'il est permis d'arreter un Ambassadeur, 4° pamp.
43. Wicquefort de l'Ambassadeur, 2 v 4°.
 7. Le Ministre public, par de la Sarraz du Franquesnay, 12°.
 8. L'art de Négocier, par Pecquet, 12°.
10. Négociations de Jeannin, 2 v 4°.
11. Ambassades de la Broderie, 1606–1611, 5 v 12°.
12. Histoire du traité de Westphalie, par d'Avaux, 6 v 12°, 1648.
13. Ambassades de Carlisle à Moscovie, Suède et Dannemarca, 12° 1660–
    1665.
14. Lettres et Négociations de Jean de Witt, 5 v 12° 1669.
15. Histoire des pormesses illusoires depuis la paix des Pyrénées, 16, 1684.
16. Recueil des traités de 1648, a 1709, de du Mont, 2 v 12°.
28. Collection of Treaties from 1495 to 1712, 2 v 8°.
29. History of the treaties of Utrecht, Gertruydenberg, Radstat and Baden,
    2 v 8° 1714.
30. The treaty of Lancaster with the Indians, 8° 1744.

31. French Memorial on the War of 1755, 8°.
44. Mémoires de la France contre l'Angletere, 4° 1756.
45. Mémˢ Sur les droits de la France et de L'Angleterre en Amerique, 2 v 4°. 1756.
17. Paralleles des Rois d'angleterre et de la France, 1758, 12°.
32. Chalmer's Collection of Treaties, 2 v 8° 1784.
33. Debrett's Collection of Treaties from 1688 to 1784, 3 v 8°.
46. Treaties of Portugal, Russia, Spⁿ. Algiers. Fr. and Gr. Br. of 1786–7, 4°. (Résultats des Traités depuis 1763, jusqu'à 1795, par Arnould, 8°) Ch. 24, N° 150. post.

Chapter 17.

Religion.

69. Sybillina Oracula, Gr. Lat. Castaleonis, 2 v 12°.
 1. King's Heathen Gods. 12°.
 2. Boyle's Pantheon, 12°.
70. Sale's Koran, 2 v 8°
71. Vetus Testamentum, Gr. LXII, Grabii, Oxon, 1719, 10 v 8°.
 3.   Id.   p. 8°.
 4. Testamentum vetus et novum, Cantab. 1665, 3 v 12°.
72. Hexaplorum Originis quae Supersunt, edente Bahrdt, Lipsiæ et Lubec, 2 v 8°.
168. Vetus Testamentum, Latinum Vulgatum, fol.
169.   ″   ″   , Lat. Junii et Tremellii fol.
73. Sacra Biblia Lovanii, Francof, 1571, p 4°.
 5. Biblia Vulgate editionis R. Stephani, 1555, p 8°.
 6. Biblia Sacra Tremellii et Junii et Test. Nov. Bezae, Amst. Janssonii, 1628. 12°.
 7. Le Vieux et le Nouveau Testaments, 12°.
156. Scott's Holy Bible and New Testament, 5 v 4°.
170. The old and New Testament, 2 v fol.

74. The Bible from the Septuagent Greek, and the New Testament by C Thompson, 4 v 8°.
75. The old & New Testament, Johnson, Philadelphia, 1804, 4 v 8°.
8. The Holy Bible and New Testament, Bowyer. Lond. 1796, 12°.
9. Liber Job, Graeco Carmine redditus, per Duport, Cant. 1653. 12°.
10. Nova Versio Graeca Bibliorum partis ex codice Veneto edita à Villoison, p 8°.
11. Lowth's Isaiah, 12°.
12. Pseaumes de David, 16.
171. Novum Testamentum, Gr. juxta Millianum, fol.
76.   "   "   " Lond. 1728, 8°.
13.   "   "   " juxta exemplar Millii, Bowyer. Lond. 1743. 12°.
14.   "   "   " Tonson, Lond. 1730. 12°.
15.   "   Thomas, Massachusett, 1800. 12°.
16.   "   "   Gr. Lat Bezae et Gall. 12°.
17.   "   "   Erasmi, Lipsiae 1578, 12°.
18.   "   "   Montani, p 8°.
77. The New Testament. Gr. Eng. 2 v 8°.
19. Novum Test. Lat Castalionis, 12°.
78. New Testament, Johnson, 8°.
172. Hammond's New Test. fol.
79. Improved version of Newcome's New Test. by the Lond. Society. 8°.
20. Codex Pseudepigraphus veteris Testamenti Fabricii 2 v 12°
21.   " Apocryphus Nov. Test. Fabricii 2 v 12°.
80. Libri Apocryphi test. vet. Junii et Nov. test. è linguâ Syriaca redditum, Tremellii, p 4°.
82. Censura Scriptorum Supposititiorum, R. Coco. Lond. 1614.
Usserius de LXX, et Liber Estherae, Lond. 1655.
Clementis ad Corinthios epistolæ. Gr. Lat. Junii, Oxon. 1633. p 4°.
83. Van Dale Dissertationes de Aristaea and Sanchoniathone et hist. baptis-morum, p 4°.
173. Hodius de Bibliorum Textibus, cui premittitur, Aristiæ historia, Gr. Lat. fol.
174. Neuman's Concordance fol.
157. Cruden's Concordance, fol.
22. Clarke's   d°.   12°.

23. Historia et Concordia Evangelica, Paris, 1653, 12°.
158. Priestley's harmony of the Evangelica, Paris, 1653, 12°.
175. Prideaux's Connections, 2 v fol.
24. Castalionis dialogi Sacri, 12°.
84. The history of Jesus by Thompson and Price, 2 v 8°.
85. Brown's Dict. of the Bible, 2 v 8°.
176. Broughton's history of all religions, 2 v fol.
25. Liturgia Anglicana, Gr. 12°.
26.   "   "   Lat. 12°.
159. The Liturgy of the Church of Eng. black letter p fol.
86.   Id.   Eng.   8°.
87. Abr. of the common prayer, 8° (Said to be by Franklin, but qu.?)
88. Form of Prayer used by the dissenters in Liverpool, 8°.
27. Heures de Cour, 16.
28. Heures, M. S. Velin, 12°.
29. orthodoxia homologia Eugenii, 24 1767.
30. Rudimenta fidei Christianæ, Sive Cathechismus. Gr. Lat. 1575. 12°.
177. Justinii Martyris opera, item. Athenagorae Atheniensis, Theophili An-
     thiocheni, Tatiani Athyrii, et Hermiae Philosophi Tractatus, Gr. Lat. Par.
     1636. fol.
31. Tertullianus, 16
178. Clemens Alexandrinus, Gr. fol.
179.   "   "   Gr. Lat. Heinsii, Lut, Par. 1641. fol.
160. Origenis Philocalia. Gr. Lat. 4°.
161. Origen contra Celsum, et de amore pulchri, 4°.
162. Origine contre Celse, par Bouhereau, 4°.
32. Lactantius, 12°.
33. Lactantius on the deaths of Persecutors, 12°.
180. Gregorius Nazianzenus, Gr. Lat. Prunaei, Coloniae, 1690, 2 v fol.
89. Sᵗ Augustine's confessions and life, 8°
181. Theodoretus, Gr. Lat. Sylburgii, fol.
90. Grabii Spicilegium. SS Partum. Gr. Lat. 8°.
182. Eusebii Evangilica preparatio et demonstratio, Gr. fol.
34. Theoriani, Leonis magni, Damasceni, Leontii et Harmenopuli disputa-
    tiones, Gr. Lat. 8°p.
91. Philo Judaeus, Gr. Lat. Pfeiffer, 4 v 8°.
92. Buchannan's Eras of Light and Christian researches in Asia, 8°.

60

93. Whitson's primitive Christianity, 5 v 8°.
94. Priestley's history of the early opinions concerning Jesus Christ, 4 v 8°.
95.   "   "   "   "   " Corruptions of Christianity, 2 v 8°.
96.   " doctrines of Heathenism and Revelation compared, 8°.
97. English's grounds of Christianity with Carey's review, 12°.
35. Austin on the human character of Jesus Christ, 12°.
163. Middleton's Miscellaneous works, 4 v 4°.
98. Barclay's Minute Philosopher, 2 v 8°
99. Furneaux's letters to Blackstone on toleration and Religious Liberty, 8°.
100. Neckar de l'importance des opinions religieuses, 8°.
36. Necessita di una religione dal Gazzera, Ital. Fr. 5 v 12°.
37. Vieilles de S⁺ Augustin, par Gazzera, 12°.
38. Les Nuits de S⁺ᵉ Marie Madeleine, par Gazzera, 12°.
183. Chemnicii examen Concilii Tridentini, 4 v fol.
164. Gregorii Cortesii Cardinalis opera, 4°.
184. Campbell's doctrine of a middle State, fol.
185. Mori opera, 2 v fol.
39. Leggenda di Giosafat, 12°.
101. Abstinence from blood defended, 8°.
40. Instructions pour les Protestants, par De la Forest, 12°.
41. Peletinage de Calvaire, 16.
42. The shortest way to end disputes about religion, 12°.
43. The Romish horse-leech by Stavely, 12°.
102. Institution de la Religion Chretienne de Calvin 8°.
44. Histoire du Calvinisme de Maimbourg, Paris 1682, 16.
45. Critique de l'histoire du Calvinisme de Maimbourg, par Bayle, Ville-franche 1683, 16.
46. Dialogues rustiques, 16
186. b. Lighfoot's works, 2 v fol.
103. The Moravians compared and detected, 8°.
104. Swedenburg on the intercourse between Soul and body, 8°.
106. Spangenberg's Christian doctrine by Latrobe, 8°.
105.   " account of the Mission of the Unitas Fratrum, among the Heathen, 8°.
107. Tower's illustrations of Prophecy, 2 v 8°.

108. Stennett's answer to Rusten on Anabaptism, 8°.

165. Barclay's apology for the Quakers, Baskerville, 4°.
109. Point de Croix, point de Couronne, par Guillaume Penn. 8.
 47. Brown's account of the Shaker's 12°.
 48. Grotius on the truth of the Christian religion, by Patrick, p 8°.
 49. Jenning's Disquisitions, 12°.
110. Paleys evidence of Christianity. 8°
 50. The Christian Panoply by Watson and Paley, 12°.
 51. Priestleys institutes of Natural and revealed religion, 2 v 12°.
 52. Officium hominis, 12°
 53. The whole duty of Man, 12°.
111. The Christian's duty, 8°.
112. Le Chrétien Philosophe, p. 4° M. S.
113. The Gentleman instructed, 8°.
114. The Lady's Calling, 8°.
115. Pascal's thoughts, 8°.
116. Pascal's life and letters, 2 v 8°.
117. Clarke on the being and attributes of God. 8°.
118. Clarke's letters to Dodwell, 8°
119. Warburton's divine legation of Moses, 3 v 8°
120. Syke's examination of Warburton's legation, 8°
121. Sykes defence of his examination, 8°
122. Welsted's Scheme of Providence, 8°
123. Sherlock on Prophecy, 8°
124. Sherlock on Death, 8°
125. Drelincourt Sur La Mort, 8°.
126. Young's estimate on human life, pamphlet, 8°
127. West on the Resurrection, and Lyttleton on the conversion of St Paul, 8°.
128. Charron on Wisdom, Eng. by Lennard, p 4°.
129.   d°   2^d & 3^d books, Eng by Stanhope, 8°.
 54. Human prudence, 12°.
 55. Les Mœurs de Panage, 16.°
 56. Steele's Christian hero, 12°
 57. Grosvenor's Mourner, 12°.
 58. Brown's religio Medici, 16.
 59. Hyldrop's works, 2 v 12°.
130. Donne on Self-homicide, 8°
131. Traité de Suicide par Jean Dumas, 8°

132. Prynne's histrio-mastix, p. 4º.
133. Nelson's comparison for the festivals, 8º
134. The Nature and end of the Lord's Supper, 8º
 60. The Sacrmᵗ of the Lord's Supper explained by the Bp. of London, 12º.
 61. Introduction to the Lord's Supper, by the Bp. of Soder and Man, 12º.
135. Baxter on justification, p 4º.
136. Observations on Waterlands defence, 8º.
 62. Societies for the reformation of Manners, 12º.
 63. Le livre des Manifestes, par Sourcesol, 12º.
 64. L'Evangile eternel, par Sourcesol, 12º.
 65. Gorton's Scriptural Account of the Millenium, 12º.
 66. a. Campbell's Something New, in 8 letters, 12º.
 66. b. The power of religion on the mind by Lindley Murray, 12º.
137. De Brahm's Time an apparition of eternity, 8º.
138. Fessenden's science of Sanctity, 8.º
139. Fish's Address and Discourses, 8º.
140. Tracts in Religion—to wit, on American bishops, Linn's Sermon, Good-rich's Sermon, 8º.
141. Pamphlets religious, 8º.
142. Religious pamphlets, 8º.
143. Pamphlets religious, 8º.
144. Witherspoons works. 2. v. 8º.
 67. Sermons de Bourdaloue, 17 v. 12º.
 68. Sermons de Massillon, 15 v. 12º.
187. Barrow's works 2. v. fol.
188. Tillotson's sermons, 3 v fol.
     Sterne's sermons, 7 v. 12º. in his works Ch. 34, No. 20. post.
145. Clarke's sermons, 10 v. 8º.
146. Clarke's 17 sermons
147. Atterbury's sermons 2 v. 8º.
148. Souths sermons 2 v. 8º.
149. Fosters sermons. 8º.
150. Sherlock's sermons. 4 v. 8º.
151. Calamy's sermons. 8º.
152. Fleetwood's sermons, 8º.
153. Price's sermons. 8º.
154. Sermons by Smith, Wharton, Shipley, Stiles, Price and others; Reports on

the Academical institution for Dissenters; Trial of Elwall for Heresy and Blasphemy, 8°.
155. M'Calla's works. (sermons) 2 v. 8°.

Chapter 18.

Jurisprudence.
Equity.

26. Kaim's principles of Equity, fol 1st. Edition.
27. Kaim's principles of Equity, fol 2^{d}. Edition.
 8. Kaim's principles of Equity, 2 v. 8°.
28. Treatise of Equity, fol.
 9. The Same, with notes by Fonblanque, 2 v 8°.
29. Francis's Maxims in Equity, fol.
10. A Treatise of Frauds, 8°.
30. Duke's charitable uses. fol.
 1. History of the Chancery. 12°.
11. Master of the rolls' office, 8°.
 2. Jus Sigilli, 16
 3. Jus Appellandi. 16
 4. Rules of the Court in Chancery, 12°.
 5. The orders of Chancery 12°
12. Rules in R. B., C. B., and Chancery, 8°.
13. Praxis almæ Curiæ Cancellariæ, 2 v. 8°.
14. Practical register in Chancery, 8°.
15. a. A Treatise on the pleadings in the Court of Chancery, 8°.
15. b. Harrison's Chancery practice, 2 v. 8°.
16. Hinde's practice in Chancery, 8°.
31. Ld. Kaim's remarkable decisions. fol.
 6. Tothill's Transactions in Chancery, 12°.
 7. Carey's reports in Chancery. 16.

32.	Finch's Reports, fol.	1673–1680
17.	Nelson's Reports, 8°.	1635–1692
33.	Cases in Chancery. fol.	1660–1693
34.	Freemans reports in Chancery. fol.	1676–1706
18.	Reports of Cases in Chancery, 3 v. 8°.	1625–1711.
35.	Vernon's reports, 2 v. fol.	1680–1719.
19.	Precedents in Chancery, 8°.	1689–1722.
36.	Gilbert's cases in the Exchecquer & Equity	1705–1725.
20.	Peer Williams's Reports, 3 v. 8°.	1695–1735.
37.	Select cases in Chancery. temp. King. fol.	1724–1733.
38.	Cases, tempore Talbot, fol.	1733–1736.
39.	Bunbury's reports, fol.	1714–1739.
21.	Atkin's reports, 3 v. 8°.	1736–1754.
40.	Abridgment of Cases in Equity, 2 v. fol.	1756.
22.	Vezey's reports. 2 v 8°.	1746–1756
23.	Ambler's reports, 8°.	1737. 1783.
24.	Brown's reports, 2 v 8°.	1778. 1789.
41.	Wythe's reports of the H. Ct. of Chancery in Vir. fol.	1795.
25.	D°. 8°.	1796.

Chapter 19.

Jurisprudence.

Common Law.

Bodies of Law—Statutes—Courts—Entries—Conveyancing— Criminal Law—Tracts—Reports.

168.	Craigii Jus feudale, fol.
169.	Lambard's Archaionomis, fol. Sax. Lat.
170.	Wilkin's Leges Anglo–Saxonicæ, Sax. Lat. fol.

1. Glanvil. 12º. 1673.
2. Glanvil, editio Totteli
   Topics on the Law of England by J. C.   } 1 v. 12º
   Noy's Compleat Lawyer
159. Bracton. 4º. 1640.
160. Fleta, 4º.
3. Britton, by Wingate, 12º. 1640.
161. Howard Sur les Coutumes Anglo–Normandes, 4 v. 4º.
171. Fortescue, de laudibus legum Angliæ, et Hengham Magna et parva, by Selden, fol.
162. Fitzherbert's Abridgment, Tottell, 1577, p. fol.
163. Broke's graunde Abridgment, 4º.
6. Finch's Law. 8º.

4. Perkins, 24.
5. Les tenures de Monsʳ. Littleton. 24.
172. Coke's 1ˢᵗ. Institute. fol.
173.   2ᵈ dº. Ed. of 1662. fol.
174.   2ᵈ. dº. 6ᵗʰ Ed. 1681. fol.
175. Coke's 3ᵈ & 4ᵗʰ Institutes, 4ᵗʰ Ed. 1670. fol.
7. Hawkins's abridgment of Coke Littleton, 12º.
176. Rolle's abridgment, 4 vol. fol.
164. Hughes's abr. 3 v. 4º.
165. Shepherd's abr. 3 v. 4º.
177. Nelson's abr. 3 v. fol.
178. Danvers's abr. 3 v. fol. A to E
179. Viner's abr. F to Y inclusive, 10 v fol.
8. Bacon's abr. 7 v. 8º.
9. Comyn's digest. 6 v 8º.
180. M. S. Abridgment, fol.
10. M. S. abridgment, p. 4º.
181. M. S. Common-place book. fol.
182. Sr. John Randolph's com. place book, M. S. fol.
12. Hale's history and analysis of the Law, 8º.
13. Delineation of the Law, 8º.
14. Glisson's Common Law epitomised 8º.
15. Jacob's common Law common-placed, 8º.

16. Jacob's introduction to the Common, Civil, and Canon Law, 8°.
17. Fulbecke's parallel of the Civil, Canon and Common Law, p. 4°.
18. Jacob's Law Grammar, 12°.
166. Blackstone's Commentaries, 4 v. 4°.
19. Blackstone's commentaries by Tucker, 5 v 8°.
20. Woodeson's Lectures on the Laws of England, 3 v. 8°
183. Spelmanni Glossarium, fol.
21. Termes de la Ley. Fr. Eng. 8°.
184. Blout's Law dictionary, fol.
185. Manley's interpreter, fol.
186. Cowell's interpreter, fol.
187. Cunningham's Law-dictionary, 2 v fol.
188. Statutes at large, 7 v. fol.
189. Ratsall's collection of statutes, fol.
190. Manby's Statutes of Ch. 1 & 2 fol.
22. Review of the Statutes, 8°.
23. Wingate's abr. of the Statutes. 8°.
24. Washington's abr. of the Statutes. 2 v. 8°.
25. Jacob's Statute-Law commonplaced, 8°.
191. M. S. Laws of Virginia of 1623–4 A fol.
192. M. S. Laws of Virginia   1629, Oct. 16—1633. Aug. 21. 43 fol.
193. M. S. Laws of Virginia   1639, Jan. 6—1642. Apr. 1. F fol.
194. M. S. Laws of Virginia   1642, 3 Mar. 2—1661, 2. Mar. 23 D fol.
195. M. S. Laws of Virginia   1660, 1. Mar. 23–
196. (M. S. Laws of Virginia   1661, 2. Mar. 23–1702. Aug. 15. Chˢ. City M. S. fol.
197. M. S. Laws of Virginia   1662, Dec. 23–1697. Oct. 21, B fol.
     (M. S. Laws of Virginia   1662, Dec. 23.–1699. Apr. 27.)
     (M. S. Laws of Virginia   1684. Apr. 16.–1692. Apr. 1. in append. to Pervis)
198. M. S. Laws of Virginia   1705. Oct. 25–Apr. 2. Charles' City M. S. fol.
199. M. S. Laws of Virginia   1705. Oct. 25–1711, Nov. 7 Rosew M. S. fol.
200. Pervis' collection of Virg. Laws, 1661. 2, Mar 23–1682. Nov. 10, fol.
201. Collection of the Virginia Laws. 1661. 2, Mar 23–1732. May 18. fol.
202. Revisal of the Virginia Laws. 1661. 2, Mar 23–1748. Oct. 27. fol.
203. Acts of the Assembly of Virginia. 1661. 2. Mar 23–1768. Mar 31. fol.
204. Code reported by the Revisors of 1776.
205. Collection of Acts and ordinances by the Chancellors. 1783. fol.

206. Draughts of bills, by a committee of revisors 1792. fol.
207. Collection of Laws. of 1794. fol.
208. A Collection of all the printed Laws of Virginia, 8 v. fol. (From 1662 to 1794)
  26. Randolph's abr. of the public Laws in force in 1796. p. 4°
  27. Collection of the Acts of the Gen. Assembly in force in 1803, and Supplement to 1812, 3 v 8°. Pleasants.
  28. Hening's Statutes, at large, 8°. vols. 1. 2. 3.
  29. Beverley's abr. of the Virginia Laws. 12°. 1720.
  30. Mercer's abr. of the Virginia Laws, 1737, 8°
  31. Mercers abr. of the Virginia Laws, 1758. 2 v 8°.
209. Acts of Congress of 1789–90–91. fol.
  32. Laws of the U. S. 8 v 8°. 1789–1808.
  33. Gilberts history of the Exchequer, 8°.
  34. Crompton on courts, p. 4°.
  35. Greenwood on Courts, 8°.
  36. Kitchin on Courts, 12°
  37. Scroggs of Courts, 8°
210. Registrum Brevium, fol.
211. Thesaurus Brevium, fol.
212. Officina Brevium, fol.
  38. Aston's entries p. 4°.
213. Brown's entries, fol.
  39. Brown's modus intrandi, 2 v 8°.
214. Brownlow's Brevia Judicialia, fol.
215. Brownlow's Declarations fol.
216. Brownlow's Entries, fol.
217. Coke's entries fol.
218. Hansar's entries, fol.
219. Levintz's entries, fol.
  40. Moyle's entries, fol.
220. Old book of entries, fol.
221. Rastall's entries, fol.
222. Robinson's entries, fol.
223. Thompsons entries, fol.
224. Tremain's (entries of) Pleas of the Crown, fol.
225. Vidian's entries, fol.

226. Winch's entries, fol.
 41. Clerk's guide by Manly, 8°.
 42. Instructor clericalis, 6 v 8°.
167. Doctrina Plactandi, 4°.
 43. Regula placitandi, 8°.
 44. Placita generalia et specialia, 8°.
227. Herne's pleader, fol.
 45. Sheppard's precedents, 8°.
 46. Read's declarations, 8°.
228. Booth's real actions, fol.
 47. Clerk of Assize, 12°.
 48. officium clericii pacis, 8°
 49. Bohun's Institutio Legalis, 8°.
 50. Bohun's English Lawyer, 8°
 51. Style's' Practical register, 8°
229. Lilly's Practical register, 2 v fol.
 52. The compleat Attorney and Solicitor, 8° (by Crompton)
 53. The Attorney's practice in R. B. by Richardson, 2 v 8°.
 54. The Attorney's practice in C. B. by Richardson, 2ᵈ v 8°.
230. Lilly's Reports, fol.
231. Cooke's reports of Cases of practice, fol.
 55. Barne's notes, 8°
 56. Powell's attorney's academy, p 4°.
 57. Book of Judgments 12° (Booth)
 58. Huxley of Judgments, p 4°.
 59. Touchstone of precedents, 8°.
 60. Curson's Arcana Clericalia, 8°.
 61. Brown's entering Clerk's vade-mecum, 8°.
 62. The Clerk's Manual, 8°.
 63. The Clerk's assistant, 8°.
 64. Trye's Jus Filizarii, 8°.
 65. Townesend's Preparative to Pleading, 8°.
 66. New Retorna Brevium, 8°.
 67. The Compleat Sheriff, 8°.
232. Dalton's office of Sheriff. fol.
233. Madox's Formulare Anglicanum, fol.
 68. The Accomplished conveyancer, 3 v. 8°.

234. Bridgman's conveyancer, fol.
 69. Brydall's conveyancer, 8°.
235. Horseman's conveyancing, 2^d and 3^d v. fol.
236. Lilly's conveyancer, fol.
237. Pigott's conveyancing, fol.
 70. West's Symboleography, p. 4°.
 71. The compleat Clerk and Scrivener's guide, p. 4°.
 72. Coverts Scrivener's guide, 2 v 8°.
 73. A book of Conveyancing, (title page wanting) 8°.
 74. Staundfort's pleas of the Crown, p. 4°.
 75. Hale's history of the Pleas of the Crown, 2 v 8°
238. Hawkin's pleas of the Crown, fol
 76. Hale's summary of the P. C.—on Sheriff's accounts.—His trial of the Witches. And on the provision for the poor. 8°.
 77. Statutes on high Treason, 12°.
 78. Foster's Crown Law. 8°.
239. State Trials, 6 v. fol.
240. State Trials, fol.
241. State Tracts (Trials) 1715–1723. fol.
242. Laud's Trial by Prynne, fol.
243. Macclesfield's Trial, fol.
244. Sacheverel's Trial, fol.
245. Trial of Elizabeth Canning, fol.
246. Trial of the Dutchess of Kingston for Bigamy, fol.
247. Trials of the Rebel Lords, fol.
248. Salmon's review of the State Trials, fol.
 79. The Criminal Recorder, 12°.
 80. Remarkable Trials at the Old-Bailey, 1st v. 12°.
 81. History of Trials, 2 v 8°.
 82. Trial of Burr, 8°.
 83. Burr's Trial by Carpenter, 3 v. 8°.
 84. Lambard's Eirenarchia, 12°.
249. Bolton's Justice, 8°.
250. Dalton's Justice, fol.
 85. Nelson's Justice, 2 v. 8°.
 86. Burn's Justice, 4 v 8°.
 87. The Justice's Case Law, 8°.

88. Webb's Virginia Justice.
89. Hening's Justice, 8°.
90. Book of oaths, 12°.
251. Wingate's Maxims, fol.
91. Buller's nisi Prius, 8°.
92. Guide to English Juries, 12°.
93. Gilbert's Law of distresses, 8°.
94.   Ejectments, 8°
95.   Tenures, 8°.
96.   Uses and Trusts, 8°.
97. Law of Bailments, by Jones, 12°.
98.   ″   ″ Commons, 8°.
99.   ″   ″ Covenants, 8°
100.   ″   ″ Ejectments, 8°.
101.   ″   ″ Evidence, 8°
102.   ″   Military of England, 12°.
103.   ″   ″   of the United States, 12°.
104.   ″ of the Army and Navy of the U. S. 12°
105. Martial Law and Courts Martial of the U. S. by Macomb, 8°.
106. Law of Mortgages, 8°.
107.   ″   ″ obligations, by Pothier, 8°.
108.   ″   ″ Trespass, 8°.
109.   ″   ″ Trover, 8°.
110. Baron and feme, 8°.
111. Goodinge on Bankrupts, 8°.
112. Billinghurst on the Statutes of Bankrupts, 12°.
113. Cooper's Bankrupt Law of America, 8°.
114. The practice of fines and Recoveries, 8°.
115. Manwood's Forest Laws. 8°.
116. Nelson's Game Law, 12°.
117. The Tenant's Law, 16.
118. The Woman's Lawyer, p 4°.
119. Somner's Treatise of Gavel Kind, p 4°.
120. Taylor's Gavelkind, p 4°.
121. Bohun's Customs of London, 8°.
252. Quo Warranto of the City of London, fol.
122. Compleat English Copyholder, 2 v. 8°.

123. Dalrymple's Essay on Feudal property, 8°.
124. Robinson's Discourse on Inheritance, 8°.
125. Ld: Kaim's British Antiquities, 12°.
126. Ld: Kaim's Law Tracts, 8°.
127. Blackstone's Law Tracts, 2 v 8°.
253. Barry's Irish Tenures, fol.
128. Spelman's Law Terms, 16.
129. Brook's Reading on the stat: of Limitations, 16.
130. Chancellor Ellesmere's speech on the Post-nati, 16.
254. Egerton's observations on Coke's Reports, fol.
131. Ld: Somers's Argument in the Banker's case, p 4°.
255. L. Raymond's Argument in B. R. in Dʳ. Bentley and Bp. of Ely. M. S. fol.
132. Annesley's Case, 12°.
133. Law-Pamphlets, 8°.
134. Law Tracts, to wit:—Varnum on paper money, and the case of Stuart and Somerset, a negro, p 4°.

135. Bellew's Richard 2, 16	1. R.2—23. R.3.
256. Keilwey's Report's, fol.	12. H.7—21. H.8.
(Dalison, with Keilwey)	1. M.—7. El.
(Dalison, with Benloe)	38. H.8—16. El.
(Benloe, with Keilwey)	6. H.8.—20 El.
257. Benloe, New fol.	32. E.3—21 El.
258. Plowden, Fr. fol.	4. E6—26 El.
259. Plowden, Eng. fol	
260. Saville, fol.	22. El.—36 El.
136. Goldsborough, p 4°.	28. El.—43 El.
261. Anderson, fol.	26. H.8—1 Jac.1
262. Moore, fol.	1. H.7—8 Jac.1
263. Lane, fol.	3. Jac.1—9 Jac.1.
264. Leonards, 2 v fol.	6. E.6—12. Jac.1.
(Owen with Noy)	4, 5. P-M.—12. Jac.1.
137. Coke, 7 v 8°.	14, 15 El.—14. Jac.1.
138. Calthrop. 12°.	7 Jac.1—15. Jac.1.
265. Jenkins, fol.	4. H.3—21. Jac1.
(Winch, with Noy)	19. Jac.1—22 Jac. 1
266. Hobart, fol	3, 4, El—23, Jac.1.

139.	Brownlow, p 4°.	4, E.4—23, Jac.1.
267.	Bulstrode, fol.	7, Jac.1—1, Car.1.
268.	Popham, fol	34, 35, E.—2, Car.1.
269.	Benloe, old fol.	6, H.8—3, Car.1.
270.	Ley, fol.	6, Jac.1—3, Car.1.
271.	Palmer, fol.	17, Jac.1—4, Car.1.
	Hetley, with Lane	3, Car.1—7, Car.1.
272.	Littleton, fol.	2, Car.1—7, Car.1.
	Bridgman with Lane.	11, Jac.1—9, Car.1.
140.	Godbolt, p 4°.	17, El—13, Car.1.
273.	Hutton, fol.	26, El—14, Car.1.
274.	Noy, fol.	31. 32, El.—15, Car.1.
275.	Croke, 3 v fol.	24, El.—16, Car.1.
276.	Wm. Jones, fol.	18, Jac.1—16, Car.1.
141.	Marche, p 4°.	15, Car.1—18, Car.1.
277.	Aleyn, fol.	22, Car.1—24, Car.1.
278.	Pollexfen, fol.	8, Jac.1—36, Car.1.
279.	Style, fol.	21, Car.1—7, Car.2.
280.	Hardress, fol.	7, Car.2—21, Car.2.
281.	Siderfin, fol.	8, Car.2—22, Car.2.
282.	Saunders, fol.	18, Car.2—24, Car.2.
283.	Vaughan, fol.	16, Car.1—25, Car.2.
284.	Carter, vol.	16, Car.2—25, Car.2.
285.	Keble, 3 v fol.	13, Car.2—30, Car.2.
286.	T. Raymond, fol.	12, Car.2—34, 35, Car.2.
287.	T. Jones, fol.	19, Car.2—36, Car.2
288.	Shower, 2 v fol.	2, W. M—4 Jac.2
289.	Shower's Parl. cases, fol.	W. M—
290.	Levinz, 2 vol. fol	12, Car.2—8, W.3.
291.	Skinner, fol.	33, Car.2—9, W.3.
292.	Comberback, fol.	1, Jac.2—10, W.3.
293.	Carthew, fol.	3, Jac.2—12, W.3.
294.	Holt, fol.	4, Jac.2—8. Anne.
142.	Salkeld, 8°.	3, Jac.1—3 G.1.
143.	Cases of removals and settlements, 8°.	9, Anne—14, G.1.
295.	Lucas, fol	8, Anne—11, G.1.

296. Fitzgibbon, fol	1, G.1.—2, 5 G.1.
144. Ld. Raymond, 3 v 8°.	6, W.M—5, 6, G.2.
297. Wm. Kelynge, fol. (2 Kelynge)	5, G.2—7, G.2.
298. Fortescue, fol.	7, W.3—10, G.2.
299. Andrews, fol.	10, G.2—2, G.2.
145. Strange, 2 v 8°.	2, G.1—22, G.2.
146. Willis, 8°.	8, G.2—32, G.2.
147. Burrow, 5 v 8°.	30, G.2—6, G.3.
148. Wilson, 3 v 8°.	16, G.2—14, G.3.
149. Blackstone, 2 v 8°.	20, G.2—20, G.3.
150. Douglass, 8°.	19, G.3—21, G.3.
151. Durnford & East's Term rep. 3 v 8°.	26, G.3—30, G.3.

152. Dallas' reports, 3 v 8°
153. Hall's American Law Journal, 8°. N° 1.
300. M. S. Cases in the General court of Virginia, fol
154. Washington's reports of Cases in the Court of Appeals of Virginia, 2 v 8°.
155. Call's reports of Cases in the Court of Appeals of Virginia, 2 v 8°.
156. Henning & Munford's reports of Cas: in the Court of Appeals of Vir. 2 v 8°
157. The Case of Campier and Hawkins in the G. C. of Virginia, 8°.
158. The Charter and Statutes of William & Mary College, 8°.

Chapter 20.

Jurisprudence.
Law—Merchant.

8. Malyne's Lex Mercatoria, 2 v. fol.
1. Jacob's Lex Mercatoria, 8°.
9. Beawe's Lex Mercatoria, fol.
10. Postlethwaite's Dictionary of Trade and Commerce, 2 v fol

7. Institutions Commerciales par Boucher, 4°.
2. Foster's digest of the Laws of Trade, 8°
3. Naval Trade and Commerce, 2 v 8°.
4. Cunningham's Merchant's Lawyer, 2 v 8°.
5.   ″   Law of Bills, 8°.
6. Marius' advice concerning bills of Exchange, 8°.

Chapter 21.

Jurisprudence.
Law—Maritime.

14. Us: et Coustumes de la Mer. Sc. Jugemens d'Oléron, Ordonnances de Wisby et de la Hanse-Teutonique, le Guidon, Assurances d'Anvers, Marine et Navigation par Cleirae, 4°.
1. Tracts on Marine Law, Sc. Schomberg on the Laws of Rhodes, Pastores, 8°.
2. Molloy de Jure Maritimo, 8°.
3. Brown's compend of the Civil and Admiralty Law, 2 v. 8°.
4. Azuni's Maritime Law of Europe, by Johnson, 2 v 8°.
15. Institutions du droit Maritime, par Boucher, 4°.
16. A Treatise on the dominion of the Sea, And a body of the Sea Laws, antient and modern, 4°.
5. La Mer–Libre et La Mer-fermèe, Analyse de Grotius et de Selden, par Champagne, 8°.
6. Barton on the freedom of Navigation and Maritime commerce, 8°.
7. Neutral rights by Jenkinson, Schlegel, Croke and York, 8°.
8. Neutral Trade, i.e. the proceedings of the U.S. on their Neutral Trade, from 1793 to 1806, 8°.
9. Pamphlets on Neutral rights—to wit, Madison, Morris, &ᶜ 8°.

10. Robinson's Admiralty reports, 8°.
11. Cooper's opinion on Sentences of foreign courts of admiralty, 8°. (Allen's Case of the Olive Branch, 2 v 8°) Post 24, nᵒ 298.
12. Clarke's practice of the courts of admiralty, 12°.
13. Id. Lat. 16.

Chapter 22.

Jurisprudence.
Law—Ecclesiastical.

17. Gibbon's Codex Juris Ecclesiastici Anglicani, 2 v fol.
 1. Examination of the Scheme of Church power in the Codex, 8°.
 2. Hills examination of the rights of the Christian church, 8°.
 3. Jura Ecclesiastica, 2 v 8°.
 4. Parson's answer to Coke, 8°.
18. Watson's Clergyman's Law, fol.
 5. The Clergyman's Vade-mecum, 2 v 12°.
 6. Degge's Parson's Councellor, 8°.
 7. Johnson's Ecclesiastical Law, 2 v 8°.
15. Burne's ecclesiastical Law, 2 v 4°.
 8. Swinburne on Wills, 2ᵈ Ed. and last published by the author himself, 4° p.
19.   ″   ″   ″   5ᵗʰ Ed. fol.
 9. Swinburne on espousals, 4°. p.
16. Godolphin's oprphan's Legacy, 4ᵗʰ Ed. 4°.
10. Nelson's Letters Testamentary, 8°.
11. Bohun's Law of Tithes, 8°.
12. Pleadings for the Marquis de Gesvres, 2ᵈ v. 12°.
13. Conset's Practice of Ecclesiastical courts, 8°.
14. Clarke's Praxis in Curiis Ecclesiasticis, 4° p.

Chapter 23.

Jurisprudence.
Foreign Law.

43. Justinian's Institutes, Lat. Eng. by Harris, 4°.
14. Justinian's Institutes, Lat. Eng. with notes, by Cooper, 8°.
44. Justiniani Institutiones, Vinnii 4°.
45. Theophili Antecessoris Institutiones, Gr. Lat. Fabroti. 4°. Paris, 1638.
15. Codex Justinianus, p 4°. Paris, Regnault. 1532.
58. Corpus Juris Civilis Gothofredi, Antwerp, 2 v fol.
16.   ″   ″   ″   ″   , Læmarius, 2 v 8°. 1598.
59. Jus Græco–Romanum Leunelavii fol. Francofurti, 1596.
46. Ulpiani Fragmenta, Notis Cannegeiter, Lug. Bat. 1774, 4°.
17. Fones quatuor juris Civilis Gothofredi, Genevæ, 1653, 4° p.
18. Vinnii Partitiones Juris Civilis, 4° p.
47. Gravinoe origines Juris Civilis, Neapoli 1722. 4°.
 1. Gravina, Espirit des Loix Romaines, traduit par Requirer, 3 v 12°.
19. Schomberg's History of the Roman Law, 8°.
 2. Les Loix des Grecs et Romains, Paris 1765, 12°.
48. Taylor's Elements of Civil Law, 4°.
 3. Zouchaei Questiones Juris Civilis, 16.
 4. Zouchaei Elementa Juris prudentiæ, 16.
20. Bynkershock opera, Lug. Bat. 1752. p 4°. 6 v.
60. Gerardi Noodt opera omnia, Lug. Bat. 1767 fol
 5. Brissonius et Hotmannus de viteri ritu Nuptiarum, ap. Hackium, 16.
61. Calvini Lexicon Juridicum fol.
62. Domat's Civil Law, by Strahan, 2 v fol.
 6. Institution du Droit François, par Argou, 2 v 12°.
 7. Projet de Code Civil par Portalis &ᶜ. 12°.
 8. Code Civil des François, 1804. 12°.
21. Code Penal, et d'instruction Criminelle, 1810, 8°.
22. Code de Commerce, 8°. 1807.
 9. Code Napoleon Civil, Procédure Civile, Criminelle, Commerce, 4 v. 16. Stereotype

23. Les ordonnances Concernant La Marine, 1786, 8º.
10. Nouveau Commentaire Sur l'ordonnance de la Marine de 1681, 2 v 12º.
11. Camus Sur la profession d'avocat, 12º
49. Arrèts de 1784–1788, 4º.
24. Tracts in Foreign Law—to wit, Contrainte par Corps, attérissemens de Gironde, Rohan, La Motte. 8º.
50. Mémoires du Card. de Rohan, la Motte, Cagliostro, &c. 12º.
12. Tracts in Foreign Law, viz. Rohan, La Motte, Cagliostro, &c. 12º.
51.   ″   ″   ″   ″   ″ Memoires in Cases of Kornmann &c 4º
52.   ″   ″   ″   ″   ″ Des Trois Roués, 4º.
53.   ″   ″   ″   ″   ″ Cases of Leris &c, 4º.
54. Mémoire de Ducrest contre le D. D'orléans, 4º.
55.   ″   ″ Reveillon, 4º.
63. Le Constituzioni Sardesche, O Carta de Logu, Sarda ed Ital. dal Mannelli, fol.
25. The Frederican Code, 2 v 8º.
64. Spotiswood's Practicks of the Laws of Scotland, fol.
26. Scotch Acts, 8º.
65.   ″   ″ From Jac. 1 of Scotland to Charles 2. fol
66. Forbes' Journal of the Sessions, fol.
67. Kaim's Dictionary of decisions, 2 v fol.
27. Judgment of the Lords of Sessions in the Case of Hamilton and Douglass, 8º.
68. Statutes of Ireland in force in 1678. fol.
28. Laws of Jamaica, 8º.
29. Abridgment of the Laws of Virginia, Jamaica, Barbadoes, Maryland, New-England, New-York and Carolina, 8º.
69. Laws of Barbadoes, New-York, Bermuda, fol.
13. Recueil des Réglemens des Colonies Francaises de l'Amérique, 12º.
70. Laws of Massachusetts, 4, W.M—6 G.2 fol.
71.   ″   ″   ″   , 4 W.M—13 W.3. fol.
30.   ″   ″   ″   , 1780–1807 3 v 8º.
31. Sullivan's History of Land titles in Massachusetts, 8º.
32. Story's Selection of Pleadings 8º.
72. Laws of Rhode Island,   1663–1718. fol.
73.   ″   ″ Connecticut,   14, Car. 2—5 G.2. fol.
33.   ″   ″ New–York,   2 v 8º

78

74.   "   " Pennsylvania.   12, W3—16 G.2. fol.
75.   "   "   "   , 1769, fol.
34. Cases of the Bank and Shoemakers, 2 v 8°.
56.   "   " Maryland, by Kilty, 3 v 4°.
35. Kilty's Maryland Landholders assistant, 8°.
76. Laws of North-Carolina, by Iredell, 1790. fol
57. Martin's revisal of Iredell's Laws of North Carolina, 4°.
36. The case of Hamilton and Eaton in North Carolina, 8°.
37. The Criminal Law of Kentucky by Toulmin and Blair.
38. The Laws of Michigan, and Tracts by Woodward, 8°.
39. Acts of the Legislature of Orleans, of 1806, 2 v 8°
40. Kerr's exposition of the Criminal Law of Orleans, 8° Fr. Eng.
41. Orleans Term reports of 1809–10, by Martin, pamphlet, 8°.
42. Laws of Mississippi Territory by Toulmin, 8°.

Chapter 24.

Politics.

General Theories of Government.
Special Governments, Antient.
"   "   Modern.*

France.	*Monarchical—Revolutionary—Imperial— her Colonies*
England.	*Constitution—Parliament—Dependancies.*
United States.	*Colonial—Revolutionary—Re-constituted— States.*
Political Œconomy.	*General—Statistics—Commerce—Finance.*

88. Platonis republica, Gr. Lat. 2 v 8°.
89. Spens's Republic of Plato, p 4°.

410. La Republique et le Phedon de Platon
                                    Par Morel, fol.

Les politiques d'Aristote.

365. Aristotle's Treatise on Government, Eng. By Ellis, 4°.

  1. Xenophontis Hiero, Sive de Regno, 12°. Foul. Gr. Lat.

  2. Xenophontis Œconomica, Agesilaus, Hieron, Lacedemoniorum et Atheniensium Politic. Gr. 12°.

  3. Hobbes de Cive. 16.

  4. Machiavelli Princeps, Agrippæ oratio contra Monarchiam, Mæcenatis oratio pro Monarchiâ, Steph. Junii Bruti vindiciæ contra Tyrannos, et de Jure Magistratuum Tractatus, 12°.

  5. Machiavelli Discorsi Sopra la prima deca di T. Livio, 2 v 12°.

  6. Lettere del Machiavelli, 2 v 12°.

366. Machiavel's works, Eng. by Farnworth, 2 v 4°.

  7. Bodin de la République, p 8°.

  8. Mori Utopia, Lat. 12°.

  9. More's Utopia, Eng. Foul. 12°.

367. Harrinton's Oceana, p fol.

411. Hooker's Ecclesiastical polity, fol.

  90. Filmer's observations on Government, 8°.

368. Sidney on Government, 4°.

  91. Nedham's Excellencie of a Free State, 8°.

  92. Political classics—to wit. Sidney, Rousseau, and More, 3 v 8°.

369. Les Oeuvres de Montesquieu. 3 v 4°.

  93. Williams's Lectures on Montesquieu's political principles, 8°.

  94. A commentary and Review of Montesquieu's Spirit of Laws, Duane 1811. 8°.

  95. Priestley's first Principles of Government, 8°.

  10. El desengano del hombre, por Puglia, 12°.

370. Ferguson's Essay on Civil society, 4°.

  96. Chastellux de la Félicité publique, 2 v 8°.

  97. Principes de la Législation Universelle, 2 v 8°.

  98. Misrim, ou le Sage à la cour, et le Roi Voyageur par l'abbé Aubert, 8°.

  11.

  99. Loix de la Nature par Poype, 8°.

100. Essay on Government by Mrs Lee, 8.

371. Della Necessita di reformare la Legislazione dal Antonio, 4°.

12. Godwin's Political Justice, 2 v 12° (N° 11 in printed Cat.)

13. Godwin's Enquirer, 12°. (N° 12 in d°)

14a. Heston's Moral and Political Truth 12° (N° 13 in d°)

14. b. Beccaria on Crimes and Punishments, 12° (N° 14 in d°)

101. Voltaire Sur Beccaria, 8°.

102. La Cretelle sur les Peines infamantes, 8°.

103. Warville des Loix Criminelles, 2 v 8°.

15. Discurso sobra las penas de España, por de Lardizabal y Uriba, p 8°.

16. Forondo sobra la Policia, 12°.

104. Colquhoun on the Police of London, 8°.

372. Howard on Prisons, 4°.

17. Bentham's Panopticon or Penitentiary, 3 v 12°.

105. Foronda de Hospitales, 8°.

106. Idée sur les secours à donner aux Pauvres Malades, 8°.

373. Instruction sur les Insensés et les Hopitaux, 4°.

107. The Penitentiary of New York, 8°.

108. Williams's claims of Literature, 8°.

18. Xenophontis Lacedæmoniorum Republica, Gr. Lat. Foul. 12°.

19. Cragus de Republica Lacedæmoniorum, 12°.

412. Petiti Leges Atticæ, fol.

20. Sigonius de Republica Hebraeorum, 8° p.

109. L'Empereur de Legibus Hebraeorum forensibus, p 4°.

21. Moyle's Tracts, 12°.

22. Hornii dissertationes Historicæ et Politicæ, p 12°.

23. Mably de la Grèce, 12°

24.   des Romains, 12°

25.   Phocion, 12°.

26.   Ordre des Sociétés, 12°.

27.   Etude de l'Histoire, 12°.

28.   Manière d'écrire l'Histoire, 12°.

29.   de la Legislation, 2 v in 1, 12°.

30.   Principes des Négociations, 12°

31.   Droit public de l'Europe, 3 v 12°.

32.   Sur les Etats Unis d'Amérique, 12°.

33.   Sur l'Histoire de France, 12°. 2 v.

34.   Principes de Morale 12°.

35.   Des Droits et des devoirs du Citoyen, 12°. Kehl 1789.

36.   Sur la Pologne, 12°.
37.   du Gouvernement et des Loix de Pologne, 2 v 12°. Paris, 1790.
38. Discours sur plusieurs Nations d' Eurpoe, d'Albon, 4 v 12°.
110. Constitutions des Principaux Etats par de La Croix, 4 v 8°.
111. Zimmermann's Political Survey of Europe, 8°.
112. Etat des cours de l'Europe, pour l'année 1788, 8°.
113. Almanach des Ambassadeurs, par Wedekind, 8°.
39. La Pologne, telle qu'elle est, a été, et sera, 12°.
114. Tracts, foreign Politics—to wit, Mirabeau, D'Ivernois, Alfieri, &ᶜ 8°.
115. Mirabeau aux Bataves sur le Stadhoudérat, 8°.
40. La ville et République de Venise, par D. S. D. 12°.
41. Liberté originaire de Venise, 12°.
374. Memoria inedita sulla Republica Veneta dal Fra Paolo, 4°.
116. Bielfield, instituciones politicas de Portugal y España, por Foronda, p 4°.
117. Constitution of the Spanish Monarchy, 8°.
118. European Pamphlets, 1794–1805 8°.
375.   ″   ″   , 1801–4, 4°.
376. Political Pamphlets, 1800–8. Sc. Dexon, Traité d'Amiens, Manifesto de
     Concija real, p fol. (French Memorial, 1757, 8°) Ante C. 16, §2. N° 31.
119. Malesherbes sur le Marriage des Protestans, 8°
120. Droit public de la France, par Lauraguais, 8°.
121. Essais politiques sur l'Etat actuel de quelques Puissances, par M. R. C. B.
     1777. 8°.
377. Tracts, to wit—Comptes rendus de 1758, à 1788, 4°.
122. Les Finances de France par Necker, 3 v 8° 1784.
123. Colonne, de l'Etat de la France, présent et à venir, 8° 1790.
124. Sur l'administration de Necker, par lui-même. 8°.
125. Almanacs Royaux, pour 1785, 6, 7, 8, 91. 5 v 8°.
126. Essais sur la Constitution des Assemblées Provinciales, par Condorcet,
     2 v. 8°.
127. Addresses, par Condorcet, 8°.
128. Opinions de Dupont, 8°.
129. Cahiers de Némours, par Dupont, 2 v 8°.
130. Tracts.—Sur les Etats Généraux, 8°.
131.   dᵒ.   8°.
132. Etats Généraux de 1789, par Brissot, 8°.
133. Résumé Général des cahiers du Clergé, de la Noblesse, et du Tiers, 3 v 8°.

134. Tracts political, French, 8°.

378.   d°. 4°

135. Tracts, King and Parliament, 8°.

379. Political Tracts, French, 87–92. 4°.

136. Procédure du Chatelet sur le 6 Octobre 1789, 8°.

137. Political Tracts, French, 1789, 8°.

138. Pamphlets, French, 1789, 8°

139. Political Tracts, French 1790, 8°.

140. Pamphlets, French, 1790, 8°.

141. Political Tacts, French 1791, 8°.

142. Pamphlets, French, 1792, 8°.

143. Débats du 10 Août 1792, 8°.

144. Procès de Louis 16, 1792 8°.

145. Pièces trouvés dans l'armoire de Fer, 1793 8°.

146. Pamphlets, French, 1793. 8°.

147. Lettres de Cart Sur le Bays de Vaud, 8°.

148. Answers to Burke by Priestley and M'Intosh, 8°.

149. Goldsmith's state of the French Republic, 1801, 8°.

150. Résultats des Traités, Supplément à Mably, par Arnould, 1803. 8°.

380. Comptes du Trésor Public, 1803, 4 v 8°.

151. Almanacs Impériaux, 1807, 1808, 1809, 3 v 8°.

 42. Essais sur les Colonies Françaises, 12°.

152. Lettres Critiques et Politiques sur les Colonies, 8°.

153. Essai sur l'administration de St Dominque, 8°

381. Tracts, French Colonies, 4°.

382. Tracts on the French East-India Company, 4°.

154. Bart sur les Colonies, 8°.

155. Des Colonies Modernes, et particulièrement de St Dominque, par Barré St Venant, 8°.

413. Discourse on Government, by Brady, fol.

414. Bacon on the Government of England, fol

156.   d°, p 4°.

157. Petty's Laws and constitution of England, 8°.

415. Acherley's Britannic Constitution, fol.

416. Tyerell's Bibliotheca Politica

417. Tracts on Constitutional questions, by Hawles, Atkins, Mackworth and others fol.

158. Historical Essay on the English Constitution, 8°.
159. Stuart's Historical dissertation on the Antiquity of the English Constitution, 8°.
160. Burgh's political disquisitions. 3 v 8°.
 43. De Lolme sur la Constitution d'Angleterre, 2 v in 1, 12°.
161. Fortescue, of Monarchy
 44. Noy's rights of the Crown, 12°
 45. Jura Coronæ, 12°.
 46. Bagshaw's rights of the Crown, 12°.
162. Burnet's rights of Princes in Ecclesiastical Benefices, 8°.
 47. Sommers' Rights of King and People, 12°.
 48. English Liberties, 12°.
163. Care's English Liberties, 8°.
 49. Brown's Estimate of the Manners and Principles of the Times, 12°.
383. Ellis's Tracts on Liberty, 4°.
418. Dugdale's Origines Juridiciales, fol.
419. Madox's Firmi Burgi, fol.
420. Brady of Boroughs, fol.
421. Spelman's works, fol.
422. Cotton's abridgment of the Records in the Tower, by Prynne, fol
423. Rushworth's collection, 8 v fol.
164. Cabala, 1ˢᵗ Ed. 4° p.
424. Cabala, 3ᵈ Ed. fol.
165. Bolingbroke's letters to Sir William Windham, 8°.
166.   ″   Oldcastle's remarks on the history of England, 8°.
167.   ″   Letters on the study of history, 8°.
168.   ″   Tracts, 8°.
169.   ″   Dissertation on Parties, 8°.
170.   ″   Patriot King. 8°.
171. The Craftsman, 2 v 8°.
 50. Addison's Freeholder, 12°.
 51. Gordon's Cato's Letters, 4 v 12°.
 52. Independent Whig, 4 v 12°.
175. Militia reformed, essay on national credit, revenues &ᶜ, 8°.
176. Tracts on Liberty and Slavery, 8°. sc. Meller, Buchanon, Webster, Tucker, 8°.
177. The Preface to Bellendenus by Dʳ Parr, Lat. Eng. 8°.

178. Political Tracts, 1707–1733, 8°.
179. Political Pamphlets, 1727–1729, 8°.
180. Papers relative to the rupture with Spain in 1762, 8°.
181. Political Tracts, 1761–8, 8°.
182. Debrett's collection of Tracts, 1763–70. 4 v 8°.
183. Political Tracts, 1769–73, 8°.
184. Pamphlets English, 1779–91, 8°
185. Tracts in English politics, 1780–84, 8°.
186. " " " " 1785–87, 8°.
187. Political Tracts, English and Irish, 1790, 1, 8°.
188. Political Tracts 1786–92, 8°.
189. Pamphlets English 1792–3, 8°.
190. Barlow, Pigot and Publicola, 1791–5, 8°.
191. Politics for the people, 1794, 5, 2 v 8°.
192. Callender's Political progress, part 2^d 8°.
193. Junius Redivivus, Letters to Pitt, Fox, &^{c} 1791–6. 8°.
194. The Philanthropist, 1795, 6, 8°.
195. Pamphlets English, 1797, 8°.
196. Political Pamphlets, Foreign, 1795–1800, 8°.
197. Political Pamphlets, English, 1800, 1, 8°.
198. Etat de la Grande Bretagne, 1804, O'Connor, 8°.
199. Political Pamphlets, English, 1804–7, 8°.
200. Political Pamphlets, English, 1804. 8°.
201. St Amand's historical essay on Parliament, 8°.
202. Gordon's history of Parliament, 2 v 8°.
203. Pettus' constitution of Parliament, 8°.
 54. Arcana Parliamentaria, 12°.
204. Hollis's Remains, 8°.
205. Hale's Jurisdiction of Parliaments, 8°.
206. Selden on the Judicature of Parliaments, 8°.
425. Petyt's Jus parliamentarium, fol.
 55. Jurisdiction of the House of Lords in Impositions, 12°.
 56. Considerations on the right of Prelates to sit in Capital Cases, 12°.
207. Brown's Privilegia Parliamentaria, 8°.
208. Petyt's ancient Rights of the Commons of England, 8°.
426. Ryley's Placita Parliamentaria, fol.
209. Prynne's Parliamentary writs, p 4°.

57. Hakewell's Mod. Ten. Parl. and method of passing bills, 16.
210. Lex Parliamentaria, 8°.
58. Orders of the house of Commons, 12°.
384. Hatsell's precedents of proceedings in the House of Commons, 3 v in 1, 4°.
427. Townshend's Historical Collections fol.
211. Determinations of the Commons in Elections 8°.
428. Bohun's Debates, Reports, &ᶜ on the Election of Members fol.
385. The Aylesbury Election, 4°.
386. Aislabie's Case in Parliaments, 4°.
387. Lound's case of the 3ᵈ auditor, 4°.
212. Ashby v. White 8°.
213. Blackstone's Case of the Middlesex Election, p 4°
429. Ephemeris Parliamentaria, or Register of Transactions of 3, 4, Car. 1. fol.
214. Debates of the Parliament of 1679, on the Popish plot, 8°.
215. Debates of 1680, 8°. Ed. 1681
216.   dº, Ed. 1725
59. Debates on abdication, 1698, 12°.
217. Parliamentary History, 1106–1660, 24 v 8°
218. Grey's debates, 10 v 8°.
219. History of the Parliament and Convocation of 1710, 8°.
220. Chandler's debates of the H. of Lords, 1660–1741, 7 v 8°.
221.   ″   ″ ″ ″ ″. of Commons, 1660–1743. 14 v. 8°.
222. Parliamentary Register 1774–7, Almon, 7 v 8°
223. Debates of the H. of Commons, in 1785, 3 v 8°.
224. Parliamentary debates of 1790. 8°.
430. Scobel's acts of the Commonwealth Parliament from 1643 to 1651, fol.
431. Votes of the House of Commons, 1727, fol.
432.   Dº.   1726–45, fol.
433. Ogle's Accounts, 1787, fol.
225. Doddridge's Works, 8°.
226. Atwood's Dominion of England over Scotland, 8°
227. State of the Union of Great Britain, 8°.
228. Mollyneux's Case of Ireland, 8°.
229. Petty's Political Survey of Ireland, 8°.
230. Debates of the Irish Commons, 2 v 8°.
231. Tracts on the English Foreign Possessions, 8°.

388. Case of the Sugar Trade, 4°.
232. Colony Tracts, 1731–3, 8°.
233. Brougham on the Colonial Policy of Europe, 2 v 8°.
389. The right of Tonnage, Duties, Fines and Forfeitures, in Maryland, fol. p.
234. Colony Titles; to wit of Pennsylvania, New York, and Vermont. 8°.
390. Hazard's Historical Collection of American State Papers, 4°.
434. The Charter of Rhode Island, Connecticut, Pennsylvania, &ᶜ fol.
391. Tracts, Britain and America; on the colonization of the Free States of Antiquity. 4°.
 60. Bougainville Sur les droits des Metropoles Grecques, 12°.
392. Tracts Political; sur les Ligues des Achéens, des Suisses, et des P. U., and DeLolme on the Union, 12°.
235. Sharpe's Declaration of the People's Natural rights, 8°.
236. Administration of the Colonies, by Governor Pownal, 1764, 8°.
237. Great Britain and America, Pamphlets from 1765–1781, 10 v 8°.
238. Franklin's Political works, 8°.
239. Reflections moral and Political on Great Britain and her colonies; with M. S. Notes by Dr. Franklin. 1770, 8°.
240. Adams's Essays, 8°.
241. Dickinson's Political writings, 2 v 8°.
242. American Gazette, Nᵒ 1. 8°.
243. Miscellanies on America, 3 v 8°. 1775–80.
244. The Remembrancer, 14 v 8°. 1775–82.
245. Tracts, Britain and America, by Price, 8°.
246. Recherches, historiques et politques sur les E. U. d'Amérique, par Mazzei, 4 v 8°.
247. Adams's Defence of the American Constitutions, 2 v 8°.
248. Observations on Government, on Adams and De Lolme, Eng, Fr. 8°.
 61. DesLandes, sur l'importance de la Révolution Américaine, 12°.
249. Triomphe du Nouveau Monde, 2 v in 1, 8°.
 62. Tracts, Britain and America, by Warville and Sinclair, 12°.
250. Mirabeau Sur l'ordre de Cincinnatus, 8°.
251. Tracts, Politics of America, to wit, Knox, Burke, &ᶜ, 8°.
252. Debates on the Constitution in the Convention of Massachusetts, 8°. 1788.
253.   New York, 8°.
254.   Pennsylvania, 8°.
255.   Virginia, 8°.

256. Debates of the Assembly of Pennsylvania, on the Bank, 1788, 8°.

257. Tracts on the American Constitution by Wilson, Martin, Pinckney, Jay, Monroe. 8°.

 63. The Federal Farmer, 12°.

 64. The Federalist, by Madison and Hamilton, 2 v 12°.

 65. Chipman's sketches of the Principles of Government, 12°.

258. Journals of Congress from 1774–88, 13 v. 8°.

435.　　″　　of the House of Representatives, 1789–93, 2 v fol.

436.　　″　　of the House of Representatives, 1789–93, 5 v fol.

437.　　″　　of the Senate 1789–93, 4 v fol.

438.　　″　　of the Senate 1789–93, 2 v fol.

259.　　″　　of the House of Representatives of the U.S. 1793–1809, 17 v. 8°.

260.　　″　　of the Senate of the United States, 1793–1809, 12 v 8°.

439. Morris's Accounts, 1781–4. fol

440. Official Reports, 1790–1. fol.

441. The Public debt, 1794. fol.

442. Public accounts, 1797–1801, 2 v fol.

443. State Papers, 1795–1809, 8 v fol.

444. Receipts and Expenditures, 1793, 4, 8, 1801, 2, 4, 5, 6. fol 7 v.

261. State papers, 1793–1812, 36 v 8°.

262. Political Tracts, American, 1784, 91, to wit, Hamilton, Murray, Logan, Leavenworth, &ᶜ. 8°.

263. Pamphlets American, 1793–4, 8°.

 66. British Treaty, and pieces on it, 12°.

264. Callender's Political register, 94, 5, 2 v 8°.

265. Pamphlets American, 1795, 8°.

266. American Remembrancer, 1795, 3 v 8°.

267. Monroe's View of the Foreign affairs of the United States, 8°.

268. Debates of Congress on the Treaty Power, 1796, 2 v 8°.

269. Gallatin's sketches of the Finances of the U.S. 1796, 8°.

270. Callender's History of the United States, for 1796, 8°.

271. Pamphlets American, 1796, 8°.

272. Pamphlets American, 1797, 8°.

393. Washington's Valedictory, 8°.

273. Proceedings of the Commissioners on the British Debts, p. 4°.

 67. Patrotic addresses to President Adams, 12°.

274. Political Pamphlets, American, 1798, 8°.

275. Callender's sketches for 1798, 8°.
276. Callender's Sedgwick and C°, 1798, 8°.
 68. Thomson's Letters of Curtius, 12°.
 69. Communications and Resolutions of Virginia on the Alien and Sedition Laws, 12°.
277. Callender's Prospect before us, 1799, 8°.
394. Mémoires sur le navire le New Jersey, 4°.
278. Political Pamphlets, American, 1799, 8°.
279.   "   "   "   1793–1800, 8°.
280.   "   "   1800, 2 v 8°.
281.   "   "   1801, 8°.
282. Callender's history of the Congress of 1801, 8°.
283. Thomson on the Liberty and Licentiousness of the Press. 8°.
284. Political American, 1791–1802, 8°.
285. Political Pamphlets, 1800–1802, 8°.
286. Old South, by Benj. Austin, 8°.
287. The United States' Claims on France, 8°.
288. Burr's case by Cheetham, 8°.
289. Political Pamphlets, 1803–5, 8°.
290. Political American, 1806, 8°.
291. D°.   , 1807, 8°.
292. The Embargo,   1808, 8°.
293. Political,   1808, 8°.
294. British Negociations, 1808, 8°.
295. Political Pamphlets, 1808–9, 8°.
296. D°.   1810, 8°.
297. D°.   1811, –12, 8°.
298. a. Capture of Olive Branch, 8°.
299. Constitutions of the States of America, 8°.
 70. ⎫
     ⎬   D°. 12°. 2 cop.
 71. ⎭
 72. Constitution of Tennessee, 12°.
 73.   "   " Louisiana, 12°.
395. Constitutions des Treize Etats Unis de l'Amérique, par le Duc de la Rochefoucault, 4°.
445. Journals of the Assembly of Virginia, 40–59, 60–74, 78–81, 84–85, 4 v fol.

300. Louisiana, 1803–4, 8°.
301. Message on Louisiana, and documents—to wit Lewis & Clarke, Dunbar, Sibley.
446. Mémoires sur la Louisiane, fol.—
302. Territories of Columbia and Michigan, fol.
303. Topographical 8°.
304. Local Politics. 1802–5. 2 v. 8°.
396. The Case of the Batture at New-Orleans, 4°.
305. Dº. 3 v. 8°.—
306. Magdalena y Yrujo, 8°.—
307. Land Companies, 1802–4 8°.—
308. Skipwith's letters. 8°.—
309. Wilkinson's Memoirs, 8°.—
310. Personal Pamphlets, 2 v 8°.—
311. Il Colbertismo dal Mengotti. 8°.
397. Stewart's Political Economy, 2 v 4°.
312. Meditazione sulla oeconomica politica dal Beccaria 8°.
313. Physiocratie de Quesnay, 2 v 8°.—
314. De l'ordre Social, par le Trosne, 8°.
315. De l'administration Provinciale, et de la réforme de l'impot par le Trosne, 2 v 8°.
74. L'ordre des sociétés politiques, par de la Rivière, avec les doutes de L'abbé Mably, 3 v. 12°.
75. La Théorie de l'impôt, par Mirabeau, 2 v 12°.
76. L'ami des Hommes par Mirabeau, 5 v 12°.
316. Ouvrâges choisis de Turgot, 8°.
317. Œuvres de Turgot, 9 v. 8°.
318. Explication du tableau économique, par l'abbé Baudeau, 8°.
319. Tracts on Commerce, Dupont &ᶜ, Notes by Dʳ Franklin, 8°.
320. Smith's Enquiry into the Causes of the Wealth of Nations, 3 v 8°.
321. New and old principles of Trade Compared, by Vaughan, 8°.
322. Traité d'Economie politique par Say, 2 v 8°.—
323. Foronda de la Economia politica, 3 v. 8°.
324. Lauderdale on the Nature and origin of public Wealth 8°.
325. Provedimenti Amnonarj dal Fabbroni, 8°.
398. Clarke on Saxon, Roman and English coins 4°.
77. Law on Money and trade, 12°.—

326. Tracts on Money, French, 8°.—
399. Essai supplémentaire à l'Encyclopédie Sur les Monnaies, par Beyerle, 4°.
400. Mesures, Monnoies, Poids, extraits de l'Enclyclopedie Méthodique, 4°.
327. Tracts on banks and paper Money, to wit, Wilson, Morris, Paine, 8°.
328. Petty's political Arithmetic 8°
329. Malthus on the principles of population, 2 v. 8°.
401. Arithmétique Linéaire de Playfair, 4°.
330. Playfair's Statistical Breviary and Commercial and Political Atlas, 8°.
331. Blodget, Statistical Manual for the U.S. of America, 8°.
332. Statistique élémentaire de la France, par Peuchet, 1805, 8°.
333. Thaarup Statistick Danske, 8°.
402. Commercia de Romani, dal Mengotti, 4°.
 78. Discourse on trade and Coin, p 4°.
 79. Pettus on trade, 12°.
 80. Gee on Trade, 12°.
 81. Tucker on Trade, 12°.
 82. Decker on Trade, 12°.
 83. Child on Trade, 12°.
 84. Condillac Sur le Commerce et le Gouvernement, 12°.
334. Prospectus du Dictionnaire de Commerce de L'abbé Morellet, 8°.
335. Montefiore's Commercial Dictionary, 8°.
336. Anderson's history of Commerce, with Coombe's Continuation, 6 v. 8°.
337. L'Intelligence du Commerce, de Malisset, 2 v. 8°.
447. Tableau du Commerce de la Russie, par le Comte Romanzoff, 3 v. fol.
338. Almanac de Commerce, par Tinna, 1808, 8°.
403. Impositions en Europe par Beaumont, 5 v 4°.
339. Recueil Alphabétique des Droits des Traités, 4 v 8°.
340. Tariff des Droits, 8°.
341. Dupont sur le traité de Commerce entre la France et l'Angleterre, 8°.
342. Reeve's history of the Law of Shipping and Navigation, 8°.
404. The Universal Merchant, 4°.
343. The Same, by Aldridge, 8°.
 85. The British Merchant, 2ᵈ & 3ᵈ v. 12°.
 86. Every Man his own Broker, by Mortimer, 12°.—
344. Biscoe's Merchant's Magazine, 8°.
345. Hoppus's Measuring, 8°.
346. The American Negociator, 8°.

405. Baldwin's British Customs, or rates of Merchandise, 4°.
347. British Rates by Sims, 8°.
348. Edgar's book of rates 8°.
448. Carkesse's book of rates, fol.
449. British Tobacco and corn Laws, fol.
450. Ld. Hawkesbury's report on the Corn Laws, 4°
349. The American Traveller, p 4°.
350. Ld. Sheffield on the American Commerce, 6th Ed. of 1784, 8°.
351. Tracts on American Commerce, 1783–7, to wit Sheffield 1st Ed., Ruston, Swan, Coxe, 8°.
352. Claviere et Warville, de la France et des Etats Unis; 8°.—
353. Swan sur le Commerce entre la France et les Etats Unis, 8°.
406. Commerce de L'Amérique par Marseilles, 2 v in 1. 4°.
407. Tract on American Commerce, to wit, Mémoire pour les Négocions de l'Orient, 4°.—
354. Tracts, American, on the commerce of the U.S. &c. 8°.
355. Coxe's view of the U.S. 8°.
356. Richesses, Dette, Finance, Population, par de la Tour, Baudeau, Coyer &c, 8°.
451. Maddox's history of the Exchequer, fol.
357. Davenant on grants and resumptions, 8°.
 87. Davis' Impositions, 12°.
358. Stevens' History of Taxes 8°.
359. Devenants reports on the public accounts, 1711. 8°.
360. Excise Tracts, 2 v 8°.
361. Gale's Essay on public credit, 8°.
408. Sinclair on the Revenues of the British Empire, 4°.
362. Tracts on English Finance, by the Earl of Stair and Craufurd, 8°.
363. Casaux sur le Méchanisme des Sociétés. 8°.
409. Political Tracts on the finances of France, England and the U.S. 1789–90, 4°.
364. Cavendish's public Accounts of Ireland, 1791, 8°.

Chapter 25.

Mathematics.
Pure. Arithmetic.

29. Hutton's Mathematical & Philosophical Dictionary, 2 v 4°.
30. Histoire des Mathématiques de Montucla & de La Lande, 4 v 4°.
 1. Histoire générale des Mathématiques par Bossut, 2 v 8°
36. Diophanti Arithmetica et numeri Multanguli. Gr. Lat. Bacheti, fo. Paris 1621
 2. Hill's Arithmetic, 12°.
 3. Cocker's Arithmetic, 12°.
 4. Pike's Arithmetic, 8°.
 5. Malcolm's System of Arithmetic, p 4°.
 6. Potter's Mathematics, 8°.
 7. Ward's Mathematics, 8°.
 8. Ward's Algebra, 8°.
31. Saunderson's Algebra, 2 v 4°.
 9. M'Laurin's Algebra, 8°.
10. Emerson's Algebra, 8°.
11. Simpson's Algebra, 8°.
12. Newton's Universal Arithmetic, 8°.
13. Saunderson's Fluxions, 8°.
14. Emerson's Fluxions, 8°.
15. Simpson's doctrine & application of fluxions, 8°.
16. Cours de Mathématiques de Wolf, 3 v. 8°.
17. Traité élémenaire de Mathématiques, par Le Moine, 8°.
18. Cours de Mathématiques à l'usâge de la Marine, par Bezout, 6 v. in 5 8°.
19. Cours de Mathématiques à l'usâge de l'Artillerie, par Bezout, 4 v. 8°.
20. Hutton's course of Mathematics, by Adrain, 2 v 8°.
32. De Moivre's Doctrine of Chances, 4°.
33. L'Analyse de la Probabilité des décisions, par Condorcet, 4°.
21. Mémoires Mathématiques de Diderot, 12°.
22. Price on Annuities, 8°.

34. Masere's principles of Life Annuities, 4°.
23.a Les Changes faits, de la Barthe, 24s.
23.b. Sir Isaac Newton's tables for the renewal of Leases, 12°.
24.a. Hewitt's Tables of interest, 16s.
35. Rowlet's Tables of discount, 4°.
24.b. Castaing's Interest book, 24s.
25. Tracts in Arithmetic—to wit, The Arenarius of Archimedes, Clavius on the Possibility of numbering the Sands, Testament de Fortuno Richard, 8°
26. Mathematical Tracts, to wit, Ricard, and Solutions of Questions, 8°
27. Hutton's Mathematical Tables, 8°.
28. Callet's Tables of Logarithms, 8° Stereotype.

Chapter 26.

Mathematics.
Pure. Geometry.

1. Tacquet's Euclid, 8°.
11. Simpson's Euclid, 4°.
12. Archimedis Opera, commentariis Eutocii Ascatonitæ, Gr. Lat. fol.
2. Archimedis Arenarius et dimensio Circuli, Gr. Lat. Wallisii, 12°.
13. Proclus's Philosophical and Mathematical Commentaries, 2 v. 4°. Lond.
3. Playfair's Elements of Geometry, 8°.
4. Géométrie de Le Clerc, 8° Paris 1774.
14. Trevigar Sectionum Conicarum Elementa, 4°.
15. De L'Hopital, Sections, Coniques, 4°.
5. Histoire des recerches sur la Quadrature du Cercle, par Montucla, 12 °.
6. Treatise on Guaging, 8°.
7. Gregory's Practical Geometry, 8°.
8. Gibson's Surveying, 8°.
9. Clendinin's Practical Surveyor's Assistant, p 4°.

16. De Brahm's Levelling balance and Zonical tables fol.
10. Adams's Geometrical and Graphical Essays 2 v 8°.

Chapter 27.

Physico-Mathematics.

Mechanics—Statics—Dynamics—Pneumatics—Phonics—Opitics.

1. Descartes, Principia Philosophiæ et Metaphysicæ, p. 4°.
2. Newton's Principia, translated by Motte, with notes by Emerson & Machin, 3 v 8°.
23. Newtoni Philosophiæ Naturalis Principia Mathematica, Comment. Le Seur, et Jacquier, 3 v 4°.
24. Pemberton's view of Newton's Philosophy, 4°.
3. M'Laurin's Account of Newton's Philosophical discoveries, 8°.
37. Boyle's Works, 5 v fol.
4. Keill, Introductio ad Physicam, 8°.
5. Martin's Philosophical Grammar, 8°.
6. Martin's Philosophia Britannica, 3 v 8°.
7. Derham's Physico and Astro-Theology, 2 v 8°.
25. Mussenbrock, Cours de Physique expérimentale et Mathématique, par Sigaud 3 v 4°.
8. Lettres d'Euler de Physique et de Philosophie, par Condorcet,—3 v. 12°.
9. Nicholson's Introduction to Natural Philosophy, 2 v 8°.
10. Webster's Elements of Natural Philosophy, 8°.
11. Adams's Lectures on Natural and Experimental Philosophy, 5 v 8°.
12. Mansfield's Essays Mathematical & Physical, 8°.
13. Mémoires Physiques de Dupont, 8°.
14. Mémoires de Physique de la Société d'Arcueil de l'année 1809, 8°.
15. Pamphlets on Subjects of Natural Philosophy, 8°.
26. Philosophical Transactions abridged, 11 v 4°.
27. Philosophical Transactions, v 74th part 2[d], 4°.

28. American Philosophical Transactions, 5 v 4°.
16. Ferguson's Lectures in Mechanics, 8°.
17. Helsham's Lectures in Mechanics, 8°.
29. Méchanique Analytique, par La Grange, 4°.
30. Bailey's Machines, 2 v 4°.
31. Recueil de Méchanique, par Person, 4°.
32. Desagulier's Experimental Philosophy, 2 v 4°.
33. Méchanique Philosophique, par Prony, 4°.
34. Architecture hydraulique, par Prony, 2 v 4°.
18. Hydraulique de du Buat, 2 v 8°.
35. D. Bernoulli, Hydrodynamica, 4°.
19. Clare on Fluids, 8°.
36. Report on the Canal between Forth and Clyde, pamphlet, 4°.
20. Tracts on Weights and Measures, 8°.
21. Newton's optics, 8°.
22. Adams's Essay on Vision, 8°.

Chapter 28.

Astronomy.

23. Tychonis Brahé Opera, 4°.
 1. Hugenii Cosmotheoros, p 4°.
24. Opere del Galilei, 3 v 4°.
 2. La pluralité des Mondes, par Fontenelle, 12°.
 3. Derham's Astro-Theology, 8°.
 4. Keill's Astronomy, 8°.
 5. Whiston's Astronomy, 8°.
 6. Gregory's Astronomy, 2 v 8°.
25. Ferguson's Astronomy, 4°.
26. Institutions Astronomiques de le Monnier, 4°.
27. De La Lande, Astronomie, 4 v 4°.
 7. Exposition du Système du Monde, par la Place, 2 v 8°.

28. Etat des Etoiles fixes de Ptolomée, par Montignot, Gr. Fr. 4°.
29. Fixarum præcipuarum catalogus novus, de Zack. 4° Gothæ, 1792.
30. Uranographie de Vaugondy 4° avec duex Cartes Celestes, pamphlet.
31. Comètographie de Pingre, 2 v in 1, 4°.
8. Figura Telluris de Maupertius, 12°.
32. La figure de le Terre par Bouguer, 4°.
9. Voyage de Rochon aux Ind. Orient. et en Afr. pour l'observation des Longitudes, 8°.
33. Deux voyages faits en Allemagne, par Cassini, 4°.
10. Mackay's theory and practice for finding Longitudes at sea & Land, 2 v in 1, 8°
11. Morden's Introduction to Astronomy, 8°.
34. Sturmey's Mariner's Magasine, fol, p.
12. Brent's compendious Astronomer, 8°.
13. Wakeley's Mariner's compass, 8°.
14. Clarke's Seaman's desiderata, by Garnett, 4° p.
15. Connaissance des Tems, pour 1777, 78, 81, 84, 85, 86, 87, 88, 89, 90, 91, 92, 93, 94, 1800, 1, 2, 3, 4, 5, 6, 7, 8. 23 v 8°.
16. Nautical Almanacs, for 1786, 87, 88, 89, 90, 93, 94, 95, 96, 97, 98, 99, 1800, 1, 2, 3, 4, 5, 6, 7, 8, 9, 10, 11, 12, 13, 14,   19 v, 8°.
17. Requisite tables for the Nautical Ephemeris, 8°.
18. Garnett's requisite tables, 8°.
19. Adams's Practical Astronomy, 8°.
20. Kunze's table of New Construction for calculating the Ecl of Sun in 1806.
21. Woodward on the Sun, 8°.
22. Tracts in Astronomy, to wit Strong's Astronomical lectures, Clap on Comets & meteors, 12°.
35. Gadbury's doctrine of Nativities, p fol

Chapter 29.
Geography.
General.

111. Dionysii orbis Descriptio, Gr. Lat. 8°, Hill.
112. Dionysii Geographia, Gr. Lat. Wells, 8°
260. Strabo, Gr. Lat. Casauboni, fol.
  1. Pomponius Mela de Situ Orbis, 12°.
  2. Solinus Polyhistor, 12° Lipsiæ, 1777.
  3. Cluverii Geographia, 24s.
261. Veteris orbis Tabulæ Geographicæ, Amstelodami, Covens et Mortier, fol.
  E. Well's Maps of Ancient & present Geography, gr. fol.
230. Atlas portatif de Grenet et Bonne, 4°.
231. Atlas by Arrowsmith and Lewis, 4°.
  F Tables Geographiques de Sanson, gr. fol.
  4. Théatre de l'univers, de Chateaunières 3ᵈ v. p 4°.
  5. Géographie de Robbe, 2 v 12°.
  6. Géographie Ancienne et Moderne de Grenet, 12°.
  7. Principes de Géopgraphie, par le Moine, 12°.
262. Moll's Geography, fol.
263. Heylin's Cosmography, fol.
232. Guthrie's Geography, 2 v 4°.
113. Pinkerton's Geography, 2 v 8°.
  8. Spafford's General Geography, 12°.
  9. Echard's classical Geographical Dictionary, 12°.
114. Scott's Universal Gazetteer, 4 v. 8°.
115. Anson's voyage round the world, 8°.
264. Harris's Voyages, 2 v fol.
  K. Collection of Maps, Geographical, gr. fol.
  L. Collection of Plans of Towns, gr. fol.

Europe.

233. Busching's Geography, 6 v 4°.

98

116. Phipp's Voyage in 1773, towards the North Pole, 8°.
10. Description de l'Island, de Horrebow, 2 v 12°.
117. Specimen Islandiæ historicum et chorographicum, per Arngrim Jonam, p 4° Amsterdam, 1643.
G Koops 10 Maps of the Rhine, the Maes and the Scheldt, gr. format, fol.
118. Marshall's travels, 3 v 8°.
119. Keyster's Travels, 4 v 8°.
120. Letters on the North, 2 ᵈ v. 8°.
234. Antonini Iter. by Gale, 4°.
235. State, Geographical, of Great Britain, 4°
121. Voyage en Angleterre, par Faujas, 2 v 8°.
122. Voyage en Angleterre par Pictet, 8°.
123. Austin's Letters from London, 1802–3, 8°.
11. The Ambulator, 12°.
12. Trusler's London Adviser, 12°.
13. Itinéraire de Dutens, 12°
124. Watson's Tour in Holland, 8°.
125. Le Guide d'Amsterdam, 8°.
126. Coxe's Sketches of Switzerland, 8°
127. Voyage en Suisse par Mayer, 2 v 8°.
128. Voyage dans le Tura, par Lequinio, 2 v 8°.
129. Voyage dans les Alpes, de Saussure, 4 v 8°.
14. Description Universel de la France, par de Hesseln, 6 v, 12°.
15. Le Voyageur à Paris, 12°.
16. Description historique de Paris, par Piganiol de la Force, 10 v. 12°.
130. Vie privée des Français, par Le Grand d'Aussy, 3 v 8°.
17. Caractère et Mœurs des Anglais et Français, 12°.
18. Tableau de Paris, de Mercier, 6 v 12°.
19. L'Espion Chinois, 6 v 12°.
20. L'Espion Anglais, 10 v 12°.
131. L'Espion du Boulevard du Temple, 8°.
21. Les Entretiens de l'autre Monde, 2 v 12°.
22. Mémoires Secrèts dun Observateur en France, tom. 22ᵉᵐᵉ. au 30ᵉᵐᵉ, 9 v 12°.
132. Fragmens Sur Paris, par Meyer, 2 v 8°.
23. Almanac du Voyageur à Paris, de 1785, 12°.
24. Curiosités de Paris, par Dulaure, 12°.
133. Ville de Nismes, 8°.

134. Introduccion a la historia Natural, y a la Geografia fisica de España por Bowles, p 4º.
236. Dalrymple's Travels through Spain & Portugal, 4º.
135. Voyage en Espagne de Bourgogne, 3 v 8º.
 25. Voyage de Figaro en Espagne, 16s.
136. Voyage en Portugal par Link, 2 v 8º.
 26. Voyage d'un Amateur des Arts, 4 v 12º.
 27. Guide pour le voyage d'Italie en poste, 12º.
 28. Voyage d'Italie de Misson, 12º.
 29. Addison's remarks on several parts of Italy, 12º.
 30. Burnet's Travels, 12º.
 31. Voyage en Italie de M. de La Lande, 9 v. 12º.
 32. Nouva Guida di Milano, 12º.
 33. Description de Gênes, 12º
237. Memoire Idraulo-Storiche Sopra la Val. de Chiana, dal Fossombroni 4º.
 34. Voyage de Terracine à Naples, par Bayard, 12º.
238. Viaggio in Dalmazia dell'Abate Fortis, 3 v 4º.
265. Pausaniæ Græciæ descriptio, Gr. Lat. Xylandri, fol. Francof, 1583.
137. Description of Greece, by Pausanias, Eng. by Taylor, 3 v 8º.
239. Randolph's Account of the Morea & Archipelago, in 1687, 4º.
 35. Voyages de Spon et Wheeler, 2 v 16s.
138. Voyage litéraire de la Grèce, par Guys, 4 v. 8º.
139. Voyage en Grèce et en Turquie, par Sonnini, 2 v 8º.
 36. Lady Montague's Letters, 12º.
140. Memoires du Baron de Tott, sur les Turcs et les Tartares, 2 v 8º.
141. Essai sur la Turquie, 8º.
266. Sandy's Travels into Italy, Greece, Turkey, The Holy Land and Egypt, fol.

Asia.

 37. Voyages de Hasselquist dans le Levant, 12º.
142. Voyage de la Troade, par Le Chevalier, avec Atlas, 4 v 8º.
143. Découvertes des divers savans Voyageurs en Russie et en Perse, 4 v 8º.
 38. Voyages et découvertes des Russes, par Muller, 2 v in 1, 12º.
240. Voyages d'Olearius et de Mandelslo, trad. par Wicquefort, 2 v 4º.
267. Voyages de Chardin, en Perse et aux Indes Orientales, fol.

241. Tableau topographique et politique de la Sibérie, de la Chine, de l'asie, et de l'Amérique, par Cordier de Launay, 4°.
39. Le Compte, Mémoires sur la Chine, 2 v in 1 12°.
242. Description de la Chine, par Grosier, 4°.
144. Compendio de las historias de la India Orient., por de la Puente, p 4°.
145. Voyage de Le Gentil dans les Mers de l'Inde, 5 v 8°.
40. Voyage de Schouten aux Indcs orientales, 2 v 12°.
146. Macintosh's Travels, 2 v 8°.
41. Poyvre sur les Mœurs et les arts de l'Afrique, l'Asie et l'Amerique, 12°
243. Mortimer's voyage to the Asiatic islands, and Canton, g 4°, Lond. 1790.
147. Woodard's Narrative of the Malays, 8°.
244. Wilson's account of the Pelew Islands, by Keate, 4°.
148. Eden's New Holland and Botany-bay, 8°.
149. Hawkesworth's account of Byron's, Wallace's, Carteret's and Cooke's (2ᵈ) voyages, 4 v 8°.
150. Cook's last (3ᵈ) voyage, 1776–9, Anonymous, 8°.
151. Ellis' Narrative of Cook's 3ᵈ voyage, 2 v 8°.
42. Ledyard's Journal of Cook's last voyage, 12°, Hartford, 1783.
152. Cook's last voyage, 4 v 8° (published by Government)
153. Capper on the passage to India thro' Egypt, 8°.

Africa.

268. Shaw's Travels, fol.
154. Voyage en Syrie et en Egypte, par Volney, 2 v 8°.
155. Lettres sur l'Egypte, par Savary, 3 v 8°.
43. Description de l'Egypte par Maillet, 2 v 12°.
245. Voyage de Denon dans la basse et haute Egypte, 2 v 4° Lond. 1802.
44. Voyage de Guinée, par Bosman, 12°.
45. Description du Cap de Bonne Espérance, par Kolbe, 3 v 12°.
156. Sparmann's voyage to the Cape of Good Hope, from 1772 to 1776 2 v 8°.
157. Bruce's Travels, 6 v 8°.
46. Relation de l'Afrique, par de La Croix, 4 v 12°.
47. Histoire de l'Afrique Française, par l'abbé Demanet, 2 v 12°.
48. Voyage de Dubois aux isles Dauphine, Bourbon, &ᶜ. 12°.
49. Voyage de Madagascar, 12°.

America.

H Ortelii Theatrum Orbis, gr. fol.
I Jeffery's American Atlas, gr. fol.
J Atlas Américain de Rouge, gr. fol.
158. Morse's American Geography, 8°.
159. Morse's American Gazetteer, 8°.
160. Tableau des Etats Unis par Pictet, 8°.
M. Birch's views of Philadelphia, gr. fol.
N. The English Pilot, fourth book, gr. fol.
50. Description des Cotes de l'Amérique, par Dassie, 12°.
51. Récherches sur les Américains, par Paw, 3 v 12°.
52. Le Lettere Americane del Conti Carle, 3 v 12°.
246. Vita e lettere di Amerigo Vespucci, 4° dal Bandini
161. Elogio d'Amerigo Vespucci, dal Canovai, 8°.
247. Purchas's Pilgrimage, p fol.
269. Hakluyt's Voyages, fol 1st Ed.
270. Collection des Voyages aux Ind. Occid., par de Bry, 11 parts in 3 v. Frank-fort.
271. Delle navigazione e viaggi raccolte, dal Ramusio, 3 v fol.
272. Hist. Universelle des Indes Occid. par Corneille Wytflict, et des Indes Ori-ent. par Antoine Magin, 2 v vol.
53. Le Voyageur Français, par de La Porte, vols 6–14, 12° 9 v.
162. Voyages de Pages autour du Monde, et vers les deux poles, 3 v in 2 8°.
54. Relation de divers voyages en Afr. et Am. par de Grande Pierre, 12°.
55. Voyage de Bossu aux Indes occidentales, 12°.
56. Nouvelle relation de la Gaspesie, par Chrestien Le Clerc, 12° 1675–81.
57. Histoire des Flibustiers, par Oexmelin, 4 v 12°.
58. Voyage au Pays des Hurons, par Sagard, 2 v in 1, 12°.
59. Voyage dans l'Amérique Septentrionale, par de Lahontan, 2 v 12°.
163. Voyages to North America, by Lahontan, 2 v 8°.
248. Lafitau, Mœurs des Sauvages Américans, 2 v 4° Paris 1724.
60. Histoire de la nouvelle France, par Lescarbot, 12°.
61. Histoire de la Nouvelle France, par Charlevoix, 6 v 12°.
164. Voyage de la Nouvelle France, par le sieur de Champlain, p 4°.
62. Voyage parmi les sauvages de l'am. Sept. par le Beau, 3 v 12°.
63. Histoire de l'Amerique Septentrionale, par de la Potherie, 4 v 12°.

102

64. Relation Ecclesiastique de la Nouvell France, 1643–4, par Vimont, 12º.
249. Adair's history of the American Indians, 4º.
165. Barton's new views of the origin of the tribes of America, 8º.
65. Carver's Travels, 12º.
166. Jones's journal to the Indian Nations, 8º.
167. Loskeil's Mission among the Indians of America, 8º.
168. Pamphlets on Indians, Topographical, &ᶜ. 8º.
66. Histoire Géographique de la Nouvelle Ecosse, 12º.
169. Present State of Nova Scotia, 1786. 8º.
67. Ogden's tour thro' Canada, 12º.
170. Mackenzie's Voyages across the Continent of N. Am. to the Pac. ocean, 2 v 8º.
273. Jeffery's Nat. and Civil Hist. of the French dominions in america, fol.
171. Lewis & Clark's expedition to the pacific ocean, 2 v 8º.
250. History of the British dominions in North America, 4º.
172. Rogers's Account of North America, 8º.
173. Voyages de Chastellux en Amérique, 2 v 8º.
174. Chastellux's voyages in America, 2 v 8º.
175. Voyage de Brissot de Warville dans les Etats Unis, 3 v 8º.
176. Volney, Tableau du Sol et du climat des Etats Unis d'am. 2 v in 1. 8º.
177. Voyage de Liancourt dans les Etats Unis, 8 v 8º.
68. Le pour et le contre des Etats Unis, par Bridel, 12º.
178. Mellish's Travels in the United States of America, 2 v 8º.
179. Tracts on America, to wit: Palairets Eng. and Fr. possessions.—Br. and Fr. Colonies—Stork's E. Florida—Barton. Nat. hist.—Examen de Chastellux—Remarks on Chastellux—Federal Lands—Ohio Company.
180. Burnaby's travels thro' the middle settlements of N. Am. in 1759–60. 8º.
181. American Farmer, by Sᵗ John de Crevecœur, 8º.
182. Cultivateur Américain, par Sᵗ Jean de Crevecœur, 2 v 8º.
183.   Do.—   3 v 8º.
69. Scott's United States' Gazetteer, 12º.
184. Roll of Officers in 1802, 8º.
70. Almanac Américain de 1784, 12º.
185. Colles's roads of the United States, p. 4º.
71. The New York Guide 12º.
186. Spafford's Gazetteer of the State of New York, 8º 1813.
187. Kalm's Travels into N. Am. by Forster, 2 v 8º.

72. Hist. de la Pennsylvanie, prise sur Kalm, et Mittelburgher, 12°.
73. Ogden's excursion to Bethlehem, 12°.
74. Maese's Picture of Philadelphia, 12°.
75. Scott's Geography of Maryland & Virginia, 12°.
188. Tracts on Virginia, and New England, by Bullock, Thomas Morton, Roberts, Coke, and others, p 4. °. 1609–71.
189. Virginia by E. W. p 4°.
190. Notes on Virginia, original Ed. 8°.
191. Coxe's Account of Carolina, 8°.
192. Bartram's Travels thro' the Carolinas, Georgia, and Florida, 8°
193. Histoire de Kentucky, de Filson, 8°.
194. Voyage à l'ouest des Monts Alleghaneys par F. A. Michaux, 8°.
195. Tracts Geographical, Elliot, Tatham, Sharp, Constable, 8°.
76. Découvertes de M. de La Sale, par Tonti, 12°.
77. Journal du dernier voyage de M. de La Sale, par Joutel, 12°.
196. La Sale's last voyage to the gulf of Mexico, by Joutel, 8°.
78. Mémoires sur la Louisiane, par Dumont, 2 v 12°.
79. Description de La Louisiane, par Hennepin, 12°.
80. Nouvelle découverte d'un très grand pays dans L. Am. par Hennepin, 1st & 3d v. 12°.
81. Nouveau Voyage d'un pays plus grand que L'Europe, par Hennepin, 12°.
251. Voyage de La Louisiane en 1720, par le père Laval, 4°.
82. Journal d'un voyage à la Louisiane, en 1720, 12°.
83. Le Page du Pratz, History of Louisiana, 2 v 12°.
197. Second voyage à la Louisiane, par Baudry, 8°.
198. Vue de la Louisiane et Floride Occidentale, par Duvallon, 8°.
199. Pike's expeditions to the Sources of the Mississippi, and thro' the Western parts of Louisiana 8°.
200. Stoddart's Sketches of Louisiana, 8°.
201. Brackenridge's views of Louisiana, 8°.
84. Gass's Journals of Lewis and Clark's journey of discovery to the Pacific, 12°.
274. { La Florida, por el Inca Garcilasso de La Vega, fol Madrid, 1723

Historia general de la Florida, por de Cardenas y Caro, 2 v fol. Mad. 1723.
275. La Florida por de la Vega, y por Cardenas y Caro, 2 v fol. (duplicate)

85. Roman's hist. of Florida, 12°.
252. Stork's description of East Florida, and Bertram's journal, 4°.
253. Ellicots Journal of the boundary of Florida, 4°.
202. Bartolomeo de las Casas, del imperio Soberano Sobre las Indias, p 4° 1552.
203. Id. Istoria della destruzzione dell Indie occid.—Span. Ital. p. 4° Venezia, 1626
86. La découverte des Indes occidentales, par Balthazar de las Casas, 12°.
204. Naufragios y commentarios de Alvar Nunez en dos jornadas à las Indias, p 4° Valladol. 1555.
87. Hist. Gen. des Indes occidentales, traduite par Fumée, p 8° Paris 1565, 1584.
88. ⎰ Historia del Mondo Nuovo, del Benzoni, Ven. 1572.⎱ 12°.
   ⎱ Bar. de las Casas, tyrannie des Espagnols, Ind. occid anv. 1579.⎰
89. Petrus Martyr Anglerius, de Orbe Novo, ed. Richard Hakluyt, p 8° Par. 1587.
205. Hist. Natural y Moral, de las Ind. por Joseph de Acosta, p 4° Sevilla, 1590.
206. Id. p. 4°, 1608–
207. Milicia y descripcion de las Ind. por Bernado de Vargas Machuca, p 4,° Mad. 1599.
90. Novæ novi orbis historiæ ex Italicis Benzoni, Latine reddita Urbani Calvetonis industrâ, cui ab codem adjuncta est Gallorum in Floridam Expeditio, p 8°.
276. Pedro Simon de Cuença, Noticias de las Conquistas en las Ind. Occid. fol Cuenca, 1626
277. Joannes de Salorzano Percira de Indiarum jure, fol Madrid, 1629.
208. Antonio de Leon, Tratado de Encomiendas &ᶜ, para las Indias, y Biblioteca orient. y occid. p 4° Madrid, 1629–30.
278. Fernan. Pizarro y Orellana, Varones Illustres del Nuevo Mondo, fol. Mad. 1689.
279. Le Nouveau Monde de du Laet, fol, 1640.
280. De Veitia Linage, Norte de la Contratacion de las Ind. Occid. fol. Seville, 1672.
281. Hist. general de las Islas y tierra firma del Mar Oceano, di Herrera, 5 v fol.
209. Gen. hist. of the Continent and Islands of America, by Herrera, 6 v 8°.
282. Description des Ind. occid. par Herrera, avec la Navigation de la Mer, fol.

283. La Monarquia Indiana, por de Torquemada, 3 v fol.

210. The Spanish Empire in America, 8°.

91. Voyages de Correal, viz. La Floride, Antilles, Mexique, N. Grenade, Guyane, Brésil, Perou, Philippines, Terres Australes, 1666–1697, 2 v 12°.

211. Voyage de La Condamine, dans l'Amérique Meridionale, 2 v 8°.

284. Hist. de la Conquista de la Nueva España, por Bernal Dias del Castillo, fol Mad. 1632.

285. Hist. de Nueva España por Hernan Cortes, fol.

92. Voyages de Thomas Gage dans la Nouvelle Espagne, 2 v 12°.

286. O. Voyage de Humboldt, 3ᵉᵐᵉ Partie Essai sur la Nouvelle Espagne et 4ᵉᵐᵉ Partie Astronomie et Magnètisme, gr. fol.

212. Humboldt's Political Essay on New Spain, Eng, 2 v 8°.

213. Notitia de la California, por Miguel Venegas, 3 v p 4°. (a copy presented to father Charlevoix)

214. Chappe d'Auteroche's voyage to California, Mexico & Newfoundland, 8°.

93. Hist. de Mexico, con el Descubrimiento de la Nueva España, por Lopes di Gomora, 12°, Anvers, 1554.

254. Hist. de la Conquista de Mexico, por de Solis, 2 v 4°

287. Viage a la Am. Merid., por Jorge Juan y Antonio de Ulloa, 4 v fol

288. Observaciones Astronomicas y Physicas, por Juan y Ulloa, fol.

215. Noticias Americanas de Antonio de Ulloa, 8°.

216. Mémoires sur l'amérique, par Don Ulloa, trad. par Villebrun, 2 v 8°.

217. Houston's Memoirs, 8°.

255. Storia del Messico dell'Abate Clavigero, 4 v 4°.

218. Voyage aux isles de Trinidad, de Tabago, de la Marguerite, et dans la Venezuela, par la Vaysse, 2 v 8. 1813.

219. El Orinoco illustrado, por Gumilla, 2 v p 4°.

95. Histoire de L'Oronoque, par Gumilla, traduite par Eidous, 3 v 12°.

96. The hist. of Miranda's attempt to effect a Rev. in S. Am, by an officer 12°

220. Description de Surinam, par Fermin, 2 v in 1 8°.

221. Histoire Naturelle de Surinam, par Fermin, 8°.

97. Voyages de Des Marchais en Guinée et Cayenne, par Labat, 4 v 12°.

222. Restauracion de la Ciudad del Salvador en Brazil, por Tamaio de Vargas p 4° Madrid, 1628.

289. Gio. Gioseppe de S. Teresa, Istoria delle guerre del Brazile, tra il Portogallo e la Olanda, fol. Roma 1698.

98. Histoire d'un Voyage fait en Brézil, par Jean de Lery, 12°.

99. Meridien de demarcation entre l'Esp. et le Portugal, en Am. par Ulloa, 12°.
100. Histoire de Paraguay de Charlevoix, 6 v 12°.
290. Commentarios reales de los Incas del Peru, por el Inca Garcilasso de la Vega, 2 v fol.
101. Historia del Peru da Pietro Cieza de Leone, Ven 1560.
    Historia del India, Ven 1566.
    Conquista di Messico da Lopes de Gomara, Ven 1565.
    La Conquista de Messico y de la Nueva España, por Lopes di Gomara, Anvers, 1554
102. Levini Apollonii Gandobrugani de Peruviæ Inventione et rebus Gestis. Antwerp, 1567, p 8°.
291. Diego Fernandez, Historia del Peru, Seville, 1571
    Augustin de Carate, Historia del Descubrimiento y Conquista del Peru, id } fol
103. Zarate, hist. de la découverte et de la conquête du Perou, 2 v 12°
104. Voyage de Marseille à Lima, par Durret, 12°.
256. Voyage aux cotes du Chili et du Pérou, en 1712, 3, 4, par Trebier, 2 v 4°.
257. Alonzo d'ovaglie, historica relacione del Regno di Cile, 4° Roma, 1646
223. Compendio della Storia del Chile, Bologna 1776, 8 (del Molina)
105. Description des Terres Magellaniques, 16s
258. Histoire des Navigations aux Terres Australes, 2 v 4.
106. Voy. Autour du Mo. et aux Terres Australes, de Dampier, et le Voy. de Wafer, 4 v 12°.
224. A collection of Voyages to the Southern Hemisphere, Magellanica, Polynesia, Australasia, &c 2 v 8° Lond. 1788.
225. Hakluyt's history of the West Indies, p 4°.
226. Oldmixon's hist. of the British Islands in America, 8°
227. Voyage d'un Suisse dans différentes Colonies de l'Amérique, 8°
107. Voyage de Labat aux isles de l'Amerique, 6 v 12°.
259. Description de Sᵗ Dominque par Moreau de Sᵗ Mery, 2 v 4°.
228. The Navigation of Sᵗ Domingo, Puységur, 8°.
108. Histoire Naturelle des Antilles, par de Rochefort 2 v 12°.
109. Histoire des Antilles Anglaises, 12°.
110. Histoire de la Jamaïque, traduite de l'anglais, 12°.
229. Edwards's hist. of the Br. West Indies, 5 v 8°.

Chapter 30.
Fine Arts.
Architecture.

P. Ruins of Balbec, by Wood and Dawkens, gr. fol.

Q. Ruins of Athens, by Le Roy, fol.

R. Ruins of Athens, by Stuart and Revett, gr fol.

18. Antichita di Roma, del Scamozzi, fol.

1. Ritratto di Roma Antiqua, 12°.

2. Ritratto di Roma Moderna, 12°.

8. Roma illustrata, Donati, 4°.

9. Vestigia é rarita di Roma, del Ficorone, 4°.

10. Varie vedute di Roma antica e moderna, del Piranesi, fol.

19. Edifices Anciennes de Roma, par Desgodetz. fol Paris, 1779.

S. Monumens de Nismes, de Clerissault, gr. fol.

T. Castell's villas of the antients, gr. fol.

20. Lubersac sur les Monumens publics, fol.

U. Monumens de Louis XV, par Patte, gr. fol.

11. Discours sur les Monumens publics, par Kersaint, 4°.

21. Plans des Maisons de Paris, par Krafft et Ransonette, fol.

22. Plans d'Architecture par Becker, fol.

12. Meinert's Schone land bankunst, or Ideas of buildings, 4° Leipzig 1798.

13. Portefeuille des Artistes, ou dessins et plans de Chateaux, Maisons, &c 4° Leipsic 1800.

V. Mitchell's Perspectives of Buildings in England and Scotland, and his gothic Architecture, Fr. Eng. gr. fol.

W. Gibb's Designs in Architecture, gr. fol.

X. Inigo Jones's and Ld. Burlington's designs, by Kent, gr. fol.

14. Morris's Select Architecture and Designs, 4°.

23. Chippendale's Cabinet Maker's designs fol.

Y. Smeaton's Narrative of Eddystone Lighthouse, gr. fol.

Z. Chambers's Chinese designs, gr. fol.

24. L'architecture de Vitruve, de Perrault. fol.

25. Il settimo libro d'architettura del Serglio, Ital. Lat.
    Regola del Cinque Ordine d'architettura, del Vignola. } fol.
    Les cinque ordres d'architecture de Scamozzi, par Daviler
 4. Scamozzi's architecture, by Leyburn, p. 4º.
 5. Architettura del Alberti, p 4º.
26. Palladio, by Leoni, with ⟨Inigo Jones'⟩ L^d. Burlington's Notes, fol.
27. Palladio, by Leoni, Ital. Fr. and Eng. 2 v fol.
28. Palladio, les quatre Livres d'architecture, par de Chambray
    Perrault's five orders of Architecture, by James } fol
    De Lorme, Invention pour batir les Couvertures courbes
15. Architecture de Le Clerc, 4º.
 6. Bibliothéque d'architecture de Jombert, partie 4me. Parallèle de l'architec-
    ture antique et moderne, par Errard de Chambray, et 2de partie Architec-
    ture de Palladio, 2 v 8º.
29. Gibb's Rules for drawing in Architecture, fol.
 3. Halfpenny's practical Architecture, 12º.
16. Elementi di architettura del Padre Sanvitali
    Elementi di architettura del Preti

    Nuove richerche sull' Equilibrio delle volte del Abate Mascheroni } fol.
    Etienne d'un ciment impénétrable à l'eau
    De La Faye sur la chaux des Romains, 8º (ante C. 15. 69)
30. Langley's practical Geometry, fol.
BB. Kirby's Perspective of Architecture, on Brook Taylor's principles, 2 v g fol.
 7. The Builder's Dictionary, 2 v 8º.
17. Dict. d'architecture civile, Militaire et Navale, par de Virloys 3 v in 2 4º.

Chapter 31.

Fine Arts.
Gardening, Painting, Sculpture.

17. James on Gardening, 4º
 9. Whateley's observations on Modern Gardening, 8º.

1. Heely on the Gardens of Hagley, &ᶜ 2 v 12°.
10. Description of Stowe, 8°.
AA. Chambers's View of Kew Gardens, gr. fol.
18. Storia delle Arti del disegno, del Winkelmann, tradotto dal Tedisco, 2 v 4°.
19. Le vite de'Pittori, Scultori e Architetti di Georgia Vasari, 3 v 4°.
2. Félibien sur les vies des Peintres et des Architectes, 5 v 12°.
11. Da Vinci on Painting, 8°.
3. Webb's Essay on Painting, 12°.
4. Gilpen's Essay on Prints, 12°.
12. Richardson's Theory of Painting, and Essay on a Connoisseur, 8°.
5. The perfect Painter, 16ˢ.
13. Galerie des Antiques à Paris, par Le Grand, 8°.
6. Galerie de Paris, 12°.
14. Annales du Musée des Beaux Arts, par Landon, 10 v 8°.
15. Le Manuel du Muséum Francais, 3 v 8°.
22. Picturesque representation of the Russians, by Atkinson and Walker, 3 v fol.
16. Dictionnaire des Monogrammes de M. Christ, 8°.
20. Ædes Walpoliana, 4°.
7. Description de l'académié de Peinture et de Sculpture, par Guerini, 12°.
23. Spence's Polymetis, fol.
24. Signa et Statua Antiqua, Perrier, fol.
21. Le Gemma Antiche figurate di Michel Angelo Causeo, de La Chaussée, 4°.
8. Antiques du Musee. 12°.

Chapter 32.

Fine Arts.
Music.

7. Holden's Essay towards a rational system of Music, 8°.
1. Jackson's Scheme of Sounds, with a Preliminary discourse, a Sheet.

2. Bremner's Rudiments of Music, 12°.
3. Rivoluzioni del Theatro Musicale Italiano dal Arteaga, 3 v 8°.
4. Burney's present State of Music in Italy, &c, 8°.
5. Burney's present State of Music in Germany, &c, 2 v 8°.
8. Geminiani's Art of playing the Violin
      Rules for playing in Taste   } fol.
6. Complete Tutor for the Harpsichord, 4°.
9. Pasquali's Art of fingering the Harpsichord
    Pasquali's Thorough-Bass made easy   }
    Zuccari's Method of playing Adagios

Chapter 33.

Poetry.

Epic.

34. Homeri Illias, Gr. 2 v. in 1 fol. Foul.
35. Homeri Odysseus, Gr. 2 v in 1. Foul.
25. Homeri Illias, Gr. Lat. cum Scholiis Didymi, 4°.
 1. Homeri Illias, Gr. Lat. cum Scholiis Didymi, 5 v 12. Foul.
26. Homeri Illias, Gr. Lat. Clarke, 2 v 4°.
14. Omero del Salvini, 2 v 8°.
 2. Homer's Illiad, by Pope, 6 v 12°.
 3. Homer's Illiad, by Mc. Pherson, 3 v 12°.
27. Homeri Illias et Odyssea, cum Scholiis et notis, Barnes, 2 v 4°.
36. Homeri, Secundum Codicem Veneti, Scholiis ineditis Villeoison, gr. fol.
28. Homeri Odysseus, Gr. Lat. Clarke, 2 v 4°.
 4. Scholia in Homeri Odysseam, 12°.
 5. Homer's Odyssey, by Pope, 5 v 12°.
29. Homer's Illiad and Odyssey, by Chapman, p fol.
30. Index Homericus Wolfgangi, 4°.
15. Fabulæ Homericæ de Ulysse ethié explicatæ, Gr. Lat. Columbi, 8°.

31. Ludgate's history of Troy, fol. 1555.
37. Virgil, fol. Foulis.
38. Virgil Servii, fol.
16. Virgil by Stirling, 8°.
6. Maphaeus's 13th Aeneid, with a burlesque Translation, 12°.
17. Virgilio del Caro, 8° 2 v.
7. Virgil by Dryden, 3 v 12°.
18. Virgil, Lat. Eng. by Pitt and Wharton, 4 v 8°.
19. Milton's Paradise Lost 1st Ed. in 10 books, p 4°.
39. Milton's Paradise Lost, fol, Foulis.
20. Milton's Paradise Lost and Regained Baskerville, 2 v 8°.
32. Milton's Paradise Regained and other Poems Baskerville, 4°.
40. La Gierusalemme Liberata dal Tasso fol.
8. La Gierusalemme Liberata, Foul. with Le Clerc's plates, 2 v 12°.
9. Tasso's Jerusalem, Eng. by Hoole, 12°.
21. Lucani Pharsalia, Notis variorum, 8°.
10.a. Lucani Pharsalia, Farnabii, 12°.
10.b. Lucan's Pharsalia, by May, 16s.
41. Rowe's Lucan, Lat. Eng. fol.
22. Quintus Calaber, Gr. Lat. not. var. de Pauw, 8°.
23. Statius, Notis Variorum, 8°.
11. Glovers Leonidas, 2 v 12°.
24. Barlow's Vision of Columbus, 8°.
33. Barlow's Columbiad, 4°.
12. Dwight's Conquest of Canaan, 12°.
13. Northmore's Washington, 12°.

Chapter 34.

Romance.
Tales—Fables.

40. Coluthi Raptus Helenæ, Gr. Lat. a Lenep, 8°.
41. Apollonii Rhodii Argonautica, Gr. Lat. Shaw, 8°.
42. Apollonius Rhodius, in Eng. verse, 2 v 8°.
 1. Achillis Tatii amores Clitophontis et Leucippus, Gr. Lat. 12°.
65. Xenophontis Ephesii Amores Anthiæ et Abrocomæ, Gr. Lat. Ital. Gall. 4°
     Lucca 1781
66. Id. Gr. Lat. Cocchii 4°. London 1726.
 2. Il Senofonte Efesio del Salvini, 12°.
67. Charitonis Aphrodisinsis de Chera et Callirhoe amoribus, Gr. lat. Reiskii
     3 v 4° Amst. 1750.
68. Caritone Afrodisieo, 4°.
43. Longi Pastorales de Daphnide et Chloe, Gr. Lat. 8° Lipsiae, 1777.
44. Amori pastorali di Dafni e Cloe, del Longo, volgorizzati dal Gozzi, 8°.
45. Lycophronis Cassandra, Gr. Lat. Reichardi, 8°.
46. Ovidii Metamorphoseon, Delp. 8°.
47. Ovidii Opera, Notis variorum, 3 v 8°.
 3. Ovids Metamorphoses, old Eng. 12°.
 4. Silius Italicus, 12°.
 5. Il Dante del Venture, 3 v 12°.
 6. Opere D'Ariosto, 4 v 16s.
69. Orlando Furioso by Harrington, fol.
 7. Don Quixote de la Academia, avec la traduction Française, 14 v 12°.
70. Gayton's Notes on Don Quixote, p fol.
48. Galatea de Cervantes, 2 v 8° Madrid, 1784.
49. Persiles et Sigismunda de Cervantes, 2 v 8° Madrid, 1784.
50. Noveles exemplares de Cervantes, 2 v 8° Madrid, 1784.
51. Viage al Parnasso de Cervantes, 8° Madrid, 1784.
 8. La Araucana de De Ercilla y Zunigo, 2 v p 8°.
 9. Les Aventures de Télémaque, 12°.

10. Les Aventures de Télémaque, Fr. Espagnol. 2 v 12°.
11. The Adventures of Telemachus, Eng. by Littlebury and Boyer. 2 v 12°.
71. Les Voyages de Cyrus, par Ramsay, 4°.
12. Gil Blas, 4 v 16ˢ.
13. Zayde par Mde. de La Fayette, 2 v 12°.
52. Corinne, ou l'Italie, par Made. de Stael Holstein, 2 v 8°.
53. Voyages d'Anténor en Grèce et en Asie, par Lantier, 3 v 8°.
54. Le nouvel Anténor par Lantier, 8°.
14. Rabelais by Ozell, 5 v 12°.
55. Ossian by Blair, 2 v 8°.
72. Chaucer, fol in Black Letter.
73. Chaucer, by Urrie, fol.
56. Chaucer, by Ogle, 3 v 8°.
15. Spencer, by Hughes, 6 v 12°.
57. Du Bartas's poems, p 4°.
16. Roderick Random, by Smollet, 2 v 12.
17. Di Lucca's Adventures, 12°.
18. Vicar of Wakefield, by Goldsmith, 12°.
19. Adventures of a Guinea, by Smollet, 4 v 12°.
20. Sterne's Tristram Shandy, in his works, 4 v 12°.
21. Sterne's Sentimental Journey, 2 v 12°.
22. The history of the Devil, 12°.
23. Brackenridge's Modern Chivalry, 12°.
24. Love and Madness, 12°.
25. Constantia Philips, 2ᵈ and 3ᵈ v. 12°.
58. The Lawyer, or Man as he ought not to be, 12°.
26. Hau Kiou Choan, or the pleasing history, 4 v 12°.
59. Il Decamerone del Bocaccio, 2 v 8°.
27. Contes Moraux de Marmontel, 3 v 12°.
28. Belisarius by Marmontel, 12°.
29. La Paysanne perverti, ou les dangers de la ville, 5 v 12°.
30. Dames Galantes de Brantome 2ᵈ v. 12°.
60. Manly's Novels, 8°.
31. Haywood's Novels, 4ᵗʰ v. 12°.
32. The Modern Story-Teller, 4 v 12°.
33. Aesopus, Gabrias, Homeri Batrachomuomachia, Aristobulus Galeomus-machia, Avienus, Lug. 1607, 16ˢ.

61. Aesopicarum Fabularum quotquot Græce reperiuntur, 8° Lipsiae, 1741.
34. Aesop, Gr. Lat. ad Usum Scholæ Etonensis, 12°.
35. Nouveau choise des Fables d'Esope, Gr. Lat. avec des notes par Le Roi, 12°.
36. Dodsley's Æsop, 12°.
62. Æsop's Fables, by Burton, 8°.
63. Phædrus, by Stirling, 8°.
64. Phædrus, by Bailey, 8°.
37. Phædrus, by Mattaire, 12°.
38. Favole è novelle del Pignotti, 12°.
39. Quatrains de Pibrac, Fables de La Fontaine et de Boursault, 12°.

Chapter 35.

Pastorals, Odes, Elegies.

41. Theocritus, Gr. Lat. cum Scholiis, 8°.
 1. Theocritus, Gr. Lat. Foulis, 12°.
42. Theocritus, Fawkes's, 8°.
 2. Teocrito del Salvini, 12°.
43. Bion et Moschus, Gr. Lat. notis Heskin, 8°.
44. Poetae Minores Græcé, 8° sc. Hesiod, Theocritus, Moschus, Bion, Musæus, Theognis, Phocylides, Pythagoras.
 3. Orpheus, Gr. Lat. 12° Trajecti ad Rhenum, 1689.
 4. Pindar, Gr. Lat. Foulis, 2 v 12°.
65. Callimachus, Gr. Foulis, fol.
45. Tyrtæus, Gr. Lat. Foulis, 4°.
 5. Psalterior, Gr. Lat. 12°.
46. Psalmi Davidici, Duporti et Buchanani, Gr. Lat 8°.
 6. Psalmi Davidici, Johnstoni, 12°.
    (Psalmorum Davidis paraphrasis poetica, Buchanani, in operibus)
 7. Anacreon, Gr. Foster.

8. Anacreon, Gr. Lat. Notis Barnes, 12°.
60. Anacreonte, Gr. Lat. Ital. del Corsini, Regnier, Marchetti, Salvini et altri, 4°.
47. Moore's Anacreon, p 8°.
 9. Anacreon and Sappho, by several hands, 12°.
10. Virgil's Eclogues, old Eng. Translations, 12°.
61. Ovidii Epistolæ, Commentantibus Volsco, Cresentinate, Parrhesio, et Ascensio, 4°.
48. Ovidii Epistolæ, Lat. Eng. by Davidson, 8°.
11. Ovid's Art of Love

    Hopkin's history of Love ⎬ 12°.

49. Ovidii Tristia, by Stirling, 8°.
12. Tibullus et Propertius, Foul. 12°.
13. Prudentii quae extant Heinsii, 16ˢ.
50. Claudian, 8°.
14. Ausonius, 12°.
15. Poetæ Latinin Minores, Foul 12° 1752, Sc. Faliscus, Nemesianus, Serenus, Calpurnius, Rutilius, Marcellus, Fannius, Sulpicia.
16. Vida 12°.
17. Poemata Italorum, 2 v 12°. Sannazarius, Amaltheus, Vida, Fracastorius, Palearius, Etruscus, Stroza, Molsa, Naugerius, Pontanus, Politianus, Ariosto, Flaminius, Augurellus, Crinitus, Cotta, Archius, Buchananus, Vaxis, Fascitellus, Parlistaneus.
18. Musae Anglicanae, 3 v 12°.
19. L'Aminta del Tasso, Foul. 12°.
20. Il Pastor Fido del Guarini, Foul. 12°.
21. Parnasa Españolo, 9 v 8°.
22. Ocios del Conde de Rebolleda, 4 v 8°.
23. Obras poeticas de La Huerta, 2 v 8°.
24. Romances de Germania de Quevedo, 8°.
25. Las Eroticas y Boecio de Villegas, 2 v 8°.
51. Pouesies Prouvencalos de Gros, 8°.
26. Recueil de Noels Provençaux, par Saboly, 12°.
27. Oeuvres de Sᵗ Evremond, 7 v 12°.
28. Five pieces of Runic poetry, From the Islandic, 12°.

62. Poems, viz. Coluthus's rape of Helen
    Joddrel's Persian Heroine.
    Humphrey's Poems   } 4°.
    Lapidary Panegyric on Fred. II. by Birkenstock
    Luzac Oratio de eruditione Altrice Virtutis Civilis
52. Ogilvie's Poems, 2 v 8°.
29. Thomson's Seasons, 12°.
66. Cowley's works, fol.
30. Cowley, by Hurd, 2 v 12°.
31. Shenstone's works, 3 v 12°.
32. Campbell's Hope, 12°.
63. Beattie's Minstrel
    The Hermit of Warkworth.   } 4°.
    Sacontala
53. Gilbert's Poems, 8°.
33. Story's power of Solitude, 12°.
34. Buckingham, 12°.
54. State poems, 8°.
55. Oldham's works, 8°.
35. The Muse in good humor, 2 v 12°.
56. Freneau's poems, 8°.
36. Freneau's poems, 2 v 12°.
37. Mrs Warren's poems, 12°.
57. Humphrey's works, 8°.
58. Discours en vers par Humphrey, Eng. Fr. 8°.
38. Rickman's poetical scraps, 12°.
64. Poems, Asiatic, 4°.
59. Poems, (Labelled Fine Arts) 8°.
39. Phyllis Whateley's poems, 12°.
40. Miss Lomax's Notes of an American Lyre, 12°.

Chapter 36.

Didactic.

45. Horace, Foulis, p 4°.
46. Horace Delphini, 8°.
 1. Horace, Notis Bond, 12°.
 2. Horace de Dacier, Lat. Fr. 10 v 12°.
 3. Horace, English by Francis, 4 v 12°.
 4. Horace, Eng. by the most eminent hands, 12°.
 5. Hurd's Horace, 2 v 12°.
47. Juvenal et Persius, Delphini, 8°.
48. Juvenal et Persius, notis variorum, 8°.
 6. Juvenal et Persius, Foul. 12°.
 7. Juvenal et Persius, Stephani, 12°.
 8. Juvenal Farnabii, 16ˢ.
 9. Juvenal, Eng. by Dryden, 12°.
10. Juvenal, Persius et Sulpicia, Lat. Fr de Marolles, 12°.
11. Persius, cum notis Bond, 12°.
12. Petronii Arbitri Satyricon, p 8°.
49. Petronius, Notis Variorum, 8°.
13. Boileau, 2 v 12°.
14. Eloge de la Folie d'Erasme, par Gueudeville, 12°.
15. Cutt's poetical exercises, 12°.
16. New Bath Guide, 12°.
17. Intercepted Letters, 12°.
50. The pursuits of Literature, 8°.
18. Cotton's Virgil Travestie, 12°.
19. Cotton's Poetical Works, 12°.
20. Hudibras, 16ˢ.
21. Trumbul's Mc. Fingal, 12°.
22. Jonathan Pindar's probationary odes. 12°.
51. Martial Delphini, 8°.
23. Martialis Farnabii, 12°.
24. Græcorum Epigrammatum Delectus, Johnsoni, 12°.

25. Græcorum Epigrammatum Florilegium Novum, 12°.
26. Epigrammatum delectus, et Elegantes Sententiæ Etonenses, 12°.
52. Anthologia Westmonasteriensis, 8°.
53. Hesiodus, Orpheus, Proclus, Gr. Lat. Ital. Salvini, 8°.
27. Virgilii Bucolica, Rami, 12°.
54. Virgilii Bucolica, Lat. Fr. par Didot, 8°.
28. Prædium Rusticum, 12°.
29. Philips's Poems, 12°.
     Darwin's Botanic Garden, 2 v 8°. (ch. 13. N° 13)
55. Darwin's Temple of Nature, 8°.
63. Lucretius, Delphini, 4°.
64. Lucretius, Tonson, Lond. 4°.
56. Lucretius, Foul. p 4°.
30. Lucretius, Baskerville, 12°.
31. Lucretius Tanaquil Fabri, 12°.
32. Il Lucrezio del Caro, 12°.
33. Lucretius, Lat. Fr. par La Grange, 2 v 8°.
57. Creech's Lucretius, 2 v 8°.
65. Drayton's Poly-olbion, p fol.
58. Manilii Astronomicon, Scaligeri, p 4°.
59. L'Astronomie, poëme par Gudin, 8°.
34. Garth's Dispensatory, 12°.
35. Armstrong's Health, 12°.
60. Armstrong's Œconomy of Love, 8°.
36. Gnomici Poetæ Græci, 12°. a Brunck. Gr. Lat. Sc. Callimachus, Callenius, Cleanthes, Eratosthenes, Evenus, Hesiod, Linus, Menecrates, Metrodorus, Mimnermus, Naumachus, Panyacides, Phocylides, Pseudo-Phocylides, Posidippus, Pythagoras, Rhianus, Simonides, Solon, Theognis, Tyrtoeus. Comicorum Sententiæ—Sc. Alexis, Amphis, Anaxandrides, Antiphanes, Apollodorus, Clearchus, Cratetes, Diodorus, Diphilus, Eriphus, Eubulus, Hipparchus, Menander, Nicostratus, Pherecrates, Philemon, Philippides, Philippus, Posidippus, Sotades, Timocles, et Monostichi ex diversis Poetis. Catonis Disticha, by Sterling, 12°. (ch. 16 §1. N° 9.
37. Carmina Quadragesimalia, 12°.
61. Pope's Works by Warburton, 9 v 12°.
38. Swift's works, 12 v 12°.
39. The World, 4 v 12°.

40. Linn's Powers of Genius, 12°.
41. Avenia by Thomas Branagan, 12°.
 Heston's Moral and Political Truth, 12° (ch. 24 N° 14).
42. Branagan's Penitentiary Tyrant, 12°.
66. The Press, by Mc Creery, 4°.
43. Virgilius Evangelisans, Rossæi, 12°.
44. Pia Hilaria Angelini Gazæi, 12° Lond. 1657.
62. Pierce Plowman's Visions. 8°.

Chapter 37.

Tragedy.

16. Aeschylus, Gr. Lat. Foul. 2 v p 4°.
17. Aeschylus, Commentaris, Scholiis et Lexico Schutz, Gr. & Eng. by Potter, 8 v 8°.
18. Sophocles, Gr. Lat. Johnson, 2 v 8°.
 1. Sophoclis Tragœdiæ, Gr. Lat. Foul. 2 v 12°.
 2. Scholia in Sophoclis Tragaedias, 12°
29. Francklin's Sophocles, 2 v in 1. 4°.
30. Euripides, cum Scholiis Gr. Lat. Barnesii, 3 v 4° Lipsiae 1778.
 3. Euripidis Tragoediæ, Gr. Lat. Canteri, 2 tom. in 4 v. 12° Heidelb. 1597.
19. Euripidis Medea et Phoenissæ cum Scholiis, Gr. Lat. Piers, 8°.
20. Euripidis Iphigenia in Aulide et in Tauris, Gr. Lat. Markland, 8°.
31. Euripides, Eng. by Potter 2 v 4°.
21. Joddrel's Illustrations of Euripides, 8°.
22. Senecæ Tragoediæ, Notis Variorum, 8°.
 4. Heywood's Seneca in Eng. metre, 12° Oxford, 1560, black letter.
 5. Opere del Metastasio, 12 v 12°.
 6. Idea de la Tragedia Antiqua, par de Salas, 2 v p 8°.
23. Shakespeare's XX plays, by Steevens, 4 v 8°.
24. Shakespear by Johnson and Steevens, with the Supplement, 12 v 8°.
 7. Dodd's Beauties of Shakespear, 2 v 12°.

32. Capell's Notes and various readings to Shakespeare, 4°.
25. Concordance to Shakespear, 8°.
 8. Dryden's Plays, 6 v 12°.
 9. Addison's works, 3 v 12° (2ᵈ wanting)
10. Otway's Plays, 3 v 12°.
11. Rowe's works, 3 v 12°.
12. Thompson's works, 4 v 12°.
13. Young's works, 4 v 12°.
26. Mallet's Works, 8°.
14. Mason's poetical works, 12°.
27. Tragedies by several hands, 8°.
15. Tragedies by several hands, 12°.
33. Operas, 4°.
28. Operas, 8°.

Chapter 38.

Comedy.

28. Aristophanes, Kusteri, Gr. Lat. cum Scoliis, fol.
16. Aristophanes, Gr. Lat. Brunck, 6 v 8°, Argentorati, 1783.
17. Menandri et Philemonis reliquiæ, Notis Grotii et Clerici, 8°.
26. Plauti Comoediæ, 4°.
18. Plautus notis variorum, 2 v 8°.
19. Plauti Selectæ Comœdiæ, Delphini, 8°.
27. Terentius Bentleii, 4°.
20. Terentius, Delphini, 8°.
 1. Poetiche del Machiavelli, 12°.
 2. Theatre Italien, 9 v 12°.
 3. Molière, 8 v 12°. (4ᵗʰ wanting)
 4. Molière, 6 v 16ˢ.
 5. Œuvres de Theatre de Diderot 12°.
21. Œuvres Complettes de Beaumarchais, 3 v 8°.

22. Œuvres Dramatiques de Mercier, 2 v 8°.
23. Comédies Françaises, 8°.
 6. Capell's Prolusions, 12°.
 7. Lilly's Plays, 16ˢ.
29. Beaumont and Fletcher, fol.
 8. Farquhar's plays, 2 v 12°.
 9. Vanbrugh's plays, 2 v 12°.
10. Congreve's plays, 2 v 12°.
11. Wycherly's plays, 1ˢᵗ v 12°.
12. Sedley's works, 2ᵈ v 12°.
24. Plays, by several hands, 8°.
13. Plays, by several hands, 2 v 12°.
14. Plays, by several hands, 2 v 12°.
15. Comedies, Steele &c, 12°.
25. Puglia's Double Disappointment, M.S. 4°.
    Jones's Sacontala, 4° (In C. 35, N° 63.)

Chapter 39.

Dialogue—Epistolary.

27. Luciani Opera, Gr. Lat. Gesneri, Scholiis et notis, 3 v 4°. Amstel. 1743.
 1. Luciani Opera, Gr. Lat. Cognati et Sambuci Annotationibus, Basil. 3 v 12°.
 2. Lucien, traduction de d'Ablancourt, 2 v 12°.
28. Mythologie Dramatique de Lucien, Gr. Fr. par Gail, 4°.
19. Erasmi Colloquia, variorum, 8°.
 3. Dialogues des Morts de Fontenelle, 12°.
20. Ld. Lyttleton's Dialogues of the dead, 12°.
21. Conversations des Gens du Monde, 12°.

Epistolary.

22. Phalaradis Epistolæ, Gr. Lat. 8°.

4. Epistolæ Apollonii Tyanei, Anacharsidis, Euripidis, Theani, Hippocratis, Democriti, Heracliti, Diogenis et Cratetis, Gr. Lat. 12°, 1601.
5. Aristenaeti Epistolæ, Gr. Lat. 12°. Par. 1610.
6. Æschinis Epistolæ, Gr. Sammet, p 8°.
7. Alciphronis Epistolæ, Gr. Lat. Bergler, p. 8°. apud Fritsch.
8. Lettres Grecques d'Alciphron, trad. en Français, 3 v 12°.
9. Ciceronis Epistolæ ad Atticum, Lat. Fr. Mongault, 6 v 12°.
   Ciceronis Epistolæ ad Familiares, (in Op.)
   Ciceronis Epistolæ ad Atticum, (in Op.)
10. Ciceronis Epistolæ ad Familiares, Lat. Fr. Prevost, 6 v 12°.
23. Cicero's Epistles, Eng. by Guthrie, 2 v 8°.
11. Plinii Epistolæ, 12°.
12. Plinii Epistolæ, Lat. Fr. par de Sacy, 12°.
24. Pliny's Epistles, Eng. by Orrery, 2 v. 8°.
13. Aschami Epistolæ, 16ˢ.
14. Lettres d'Abeillard et d'Héloïse, par Dom Gervaise, Lat. Fr. 2 v 12°.
15. La vie d'Abeillard et d'Héloïse, par Dom Gervaise, 12°.
25. Le Blanc's Letters, 2 v 8°.
16. Œuvres de Voiture, 12°.
26. Lettres de Mad. de Sévigné, 8 v 8°. Paris 1806.
17. Nouveau Manuel Epistolaire, 12°.
18. Ignatius Sancho's Letters, 12°.

Chapter 40.

Logic, Rhetoric, Orations.

Aristotelis Logica, Gr. Lat. Pacii, (in Op.)
13. Wallis Institutio Logicæ, 8°.
14. Crackanthorpii Logica, 4°.
 1. Artis Logicæ, Aldrich, 12°.
15. Watt's Logic, 8°.

16. Logica de Condillac, par Foronda, 8°.
 2. The Logic of Condillac, by Neef, p 8°.
17. Fraunces's Lawyer's Logic, 4°.

Rhetoric.

Aristotelis Rhetorica, Gr. Lat. Riceoboni, (in op.)
 3. Vossii Rhetorica, 12°.
 4. Dugard Rhetorices Elementa, 12°.
18. Quinctiliani Institutiones Oratoriæ, 4°.
19. Ward's Oratory, 2 v 8°.
20. Blair's Lectures on Rhetoric, 3 v 8°.
21. Adams's Lectures on Rhetoric and Oratory, 2 v 8°.
22. Cicero's Orator, by Guthrie, 8°.
23. Demetrius Phalereus de Elocutione, Gr. Lat. Foul. 8°.
 5. Cambray on Eloquence, 12°.
24. Sheridan on Elocution, 8°.
25. Mason on Poetical and Prosaic Numbers, and Elocution, 8°.

Orations.

26. Demosthenes, Æschines, Deinarchus, Lycurgus, Demades, Gr. Ando-
    cides, Lysias, Isaeus, Antiphon, Gr. Lat. Lesbonactes, Herodes, Antis-
    thenes, Alcidamas, et Georgias, Gr. Notis Wolfii, Taylori, Markland, et
    Jacobi Reiske, 22 v 8°. Lipsiæ 1770–1775, Cui additur, Oratio Inedita Isaei
    Rhetoris.
27. Demosthenis Orationes Selectæ, Mounteney, 8°.
28. Œuvres de Démosthène et d'Eschine, par Auger, Fr. 5 v 8°.
 6. Demosthenis Philippica, Gr. Foul. Eng. by Several, 2 v 12°.
 7. Æschynis in Ctesiphontem Oratio.
 8. Lycurgi Oratio, Gr. Lat. 12°.
29. Discours de Lycurgue, d'Andocide, &ᶜ par Auger, Fr. 8°.
30. Isocratis Orationes, Gr. 2 v 8°.
31. Isocrate d'Auger, 3 v 8°.
32. Isocrates's Orations, Eng. by Dinsdale, 8°.
33. Cicero's Orations, Eng. by Guthrie, 3 v 8°.
 9. Histoire des Discours de Cicéron, 12°. Paris 1765.
10. Orationes ex Historicis excerptæ, 12°.

34. Quinctiliani Declamationes, 8°.
35. Curran's Forensic Eloquence, 8°.
36. Orations—to wit, Inauguralis of Ezra Stiles, de Antiqua Medico-Philosophia à Coste, Inauguralis de Cholera a Lyons, on the influence of Physical Causes, &ᶜ by Rush, 8°.
37. Eulogiums on Washington, 8°.
38. Orations of the 4ᵗʰ of July, 8°.
11. Orations on the Massacre at Boston of March 5 1770. 12°.
39. Oration by Fairfax 8°.
12. Birch's Virginian Orator, 12°.
    The Boylston Prize Dissertations, by Shattuck, 8°. (Ante C. 10. Nᵒ 87)

Chapter 41.

Criticism.
Theory.

1. Aristotle de Arte Poetica, Gr. Lat. 12°. Foul.
2. La Poetica de Aristoteles por das Saijas, Gr. Lat. Span. p. 8°.
13. Longinus de Sublimitate, Gr. Lat. 4°. Tollii.
3. Longinus de Sublimitate, Gr. Lat. 12°.
7. Rapin's Critical Works, Eng. 2 v 8°.
14. Théorie Circonsphérique de deux Genres du Beau, par Cordier de Launay, 4°.
8. Kaim's Elements of Criticism, 2 v 8°.
9. Fitzosborne's Letters, 8°.
4. Du Bos sur la Poésie et la Peinture, 3 v 12°.
10. Geddes on the Composition of the Ancients, 8°.
5. Trapp's Prælectiones poeticæ, 2d. v. 12°.
6. Franklyn on the Antient Tragedy, 12°.
11. Riccoboni's Account of the Theatres in Europe, 8°.
12. Harris's Philological Enquiries, 8°.

Chapter 42.

Criticism
Bibliography.

 7. Jones, Poeseos Asiaticæ Commentaria, 8°.

 8. Lowth de Poesi Hebraeorum, 8°.

 1. Blackwell on the Sacred Classics, 2 v 12°.

 2. Blackwell on the Classics, 12°.

 9. Vossius de Historicis Græcis, p 4°.

10. Vossius de Historicis Latinis, p 4°.

11. Fabricii Bibliotheca Latina, 8°.

3a. Bibliothéque Choisie, 28 v 12° (3ᵈ wanting)

3b. Bibliothéque des Sciences et des Arts, 63 v 12°.

12. Nicholson's Historical Library, 8°.

 4. Whear de Methodo Legendi historias, 12°.

13. Essay on Shakespeare by Mʳˢ Montague, 8°.

 5. Richardson's Analysis of Shakespeare's characters, 12°.

14. Warton's Observations on Spencer, 2 v 8°.

15. Aristarchus Anti Bentleianus, by Johnson, 8°.

16. Monthly Review, 31 v to 1764 and 1786, 7, 8, 4v. 35 v 8°.

17. Ayscough's Index to the Monthly Review, from 1749 to 1784, 2 v 8°.

18. Critical Reviews for 1786, 7, 8, 3 v 8°.

19. The Edinburgh Review, 7 v 8°.

20. Bibliographie Instructive de De Bure, 9 v 8°.

21. Annuaire de la Librairie, par Fleischer, 8°.

22. Alber's American Annals in Physics, Chemistry, &ᶜ 12° 1803.

 6. Worral's Catalogue of Law Books, 12°.

23. Miller's Retrospect of the 18ᵗʰ Century, 2 v 8°.

Chapter 43.

Criticism
Languages.

Cadmus, by Thornton, 8° (See C. 15. N° 39).

  51. Harris's Hermes, 8°.

101. Linguarum totius orbis Vocabularia, a Pallas, 2 v 4°.

102. Vocabulaires Comparés des Langues de Toute La Terre, par Pallas. 4 v 4°.

128. Calepini Dictionarium VII Linguarum—Sc. Lat. Heb. Gr. Gal. Ital. Germ. Hisp. fol.

129. Calepini Dictionarium XI. Linguarum,—sc. Lat. &ᶜ et Ang. Belg. Pol. Ungar. fol.

  52. Gurtleri Lexicon IV. Linguarum—sc. Lat Gr. Gal. Germ. 8°.

130. Minshieu's Guide into the tongues, XI. Sc. Ang. Belg. Germ. Gal. Ital. Hisp. Lat. Gr. Hebr. fol.

  53. Oratio Dominica in diversas linguas versa, a Chamberlayne, p 4°.

  54. Sennarti Chaldaismus et Syriasmus, p. 4°.

   1. Erpenii Rudimenta linguæ Arabicæ, Lug. Bat. 1628. 12°.

  55. Simplification des langues Arabe, Persanne et Turque, par Volney, 8°.

103. Specimina Arabica et Persica, a Vieyra, 4°.

131. *Euclidis Elementorum Libri XIII, Arabicè, Romæ, 1594. fol.

   2. Evangelium Infantiae. Servatorio, Arabice et Latine, Sykes, 12°.

   3. Indian or Bengal Vocabulary, 12°.

  56. Portroyal Greek Grammar, French, 8°.

  57. Graecæ Grammaticæ Institutiones, Edinburgh, (Ruddiman) 8°.

   4. Westminster Greek Grammar, 8°.

  58. Grammatica Græca, Eton, 8°.

  59. Grammatica Busbeiana Græca, 8°.

  60. Elementa Linguæ Græcæ, Moor, 8°.

  61. Holmes's Greek Grammar, 8°.

  62. Greek Grammar of Gloucester, 8°.

---

*Books in rare Languages are classed here, not according to their subject-matter, but philologically, as Specimens of the Language in which they are written.

5. Le jardin des Racines Grecques, de Claude Lancelot de Portroyal, 12°.
132. Stephani Thesaurus Linguæ Græcæ, 4 v fol.
133. Scapulæ Lexicon, fol.
104. Scapulæ Lexicon, 4° Læmarii, 1598.
105. Hederici Lexicon, 4°.
134. Etymologium Magnum Græcum, fol.
135. Julii Pollucis Onomasticon, 2 v in 1. fol.
136. Suidæ Lexicon, Gr. Lat. Kusteri, 3 v fol.
6. Dugard Lexicon Græci Testamenti, p 8°.
7. Pasoris Manuale Græci Testamenti, 12°.
106. Parkhursts Greek and English Lexicon, 4°.
63. Clavis Homerica, 8°.
64. Wetstenii orationes de Linguæ Græcae Pronunciatione &ᶜ 8°.
8. Devarii de Particulis Græcis. 16ˢ.
9. Kusterus de Verbo Medio, 12°.
10. Viger Rotomagensis de Græcæ dictionis idiotismis, Par. 1627, 12°.
137. Basilii Fabri Thesaurus Eruditionis Scholasticæ, fol.
138. Glossarium mediæ et infimae græcitatis, Dufresne dominus du Cange. 2 v fol.
107. Meursii Glossarium Græco-barbarum, 4°.
108. Dizzionario Greco-volgare et Italiano, dal Somavera, 2 v 4° Parigi, 1709.
65. Sanctius de Causis Linguæ Latinæ, 8°.
66. The Portroyal Latin Grammar, Fr. 8°.
11. Abrégé de la Nouvelle Méthode Latine de Portroyal, 8. p.
67. Ruddimanni Institutiones Grammaticæ Latinæ, 8°.
12. Ruddiman's Rudiments of the Latin, 12°.
13. Lilly's Latin Grammar, 12°.
68. Latin Grammar, 8°.
14. Clarke's Latin Grammar, 12°.
15. Ross's Latin Grammar, 12°.
16. Smith's New-Hampshire Latin Grammar, 8°.
139. Stephani Thesaurus Linguæ Latinæ, 2 v fol.
140. Vossii Etymologicon Romanum, fol.
141. Thesaurus Linguæ Latinæ, Cooper, fol.
142. Holyoke's Dictionary, Lat. Eng. fol.
109. Ainsworth's Dictionary, Lat. Eng. 3 v 4°.
69. Ainsworth's Lat. and Eng. Dic. Abridged, 2 v 8°.

110. Littleton's Eng.-Lat., Poetical, Historical, Geographical, and Latino-barbarous Dic.

70. Clavis Virgiliana, 8°.

71. Anchorani Porta Linguarum Trilinguis, 8°.

72. Robertson's Latin Phrases, 8°.

17. Gradus ad Parnassum, Gr. 12°.

18. Hoole's Accidence, 12°.

73. Sententiæ Pueriles, 8°.

19. Corderii Colloquia, Lat. Fr. 12°.

20. Stirling's Exercises, 12°.

74. Della Lingua Toscana del Buommatei, p 4°.

21. Grammaire Italienne d'Antonini, 12°.

143. Vocabolario della Crusca, 5 v fol.

111. Vocabolario della Crusca, Ven 1741, 5 tom in 2 v 4°.

112. Dictionnaire Ital et Franc. d'Alberti, 2 v 4°.

113. Baretti's Dictionary, Ital. Eng. 2 v 4°.

22. Bottarelli's Dictionary, Ital. Fr. Eng. 3 v 12°.

23. Grammatica Castellana por l'Academia, 12°.

75. Grammaire Espagnole de Pellizer, 8°.

144. Diccionario de Academia Espagnolo, fol.

114. Dictionaire Espagnol, Français, Latin, de Sejournant, 2 v 4°.

145. Baretti's Spanish and Eng. Dictionary, 2 v fol.

76. Trésor des trois Langues, Espag. Franc. Ital. 3 v p 4°.

77. Dictionnaire portatif et de prononciation, Esp. Frans. par Cormon. 2 v 8°.

24. Diccionario portatil, Span & Eng. 2 v 12°.

78. Dictionnaire Languedocien-Français, par L. D. S. 8°.

79. Dufief's Nature Displayed, Adapted to the French Language, 2 v 8°.

115. Dictionnaire de l'Académie Français, 2 v in 1. 4°.

146. Dictionnaire de Trévouse, 8 v fol. Par. 1771.

147. Dictionaire de Richelet, 3 v fol.

148. Dictionnaire Etymologique de la Langue Francaise, de Ménage, 2 v fol.

80. Dictionnaire Etymologique, par Morin, 8°.

81. Dictionnaire du Vieux Langage, de La Combe, 2 v 8°.

25. Dictionnaire Néologique Français, par Snetlage, 12°.

116. Dictionnaire Franc. Ang. de Chambaud et Robinet, 2 v 4°.

149. Dictionnaire Franc. Ang. de Miege, fol.

82. Dictionary, Fr. Eng. by Dufief. 3 v 8°.

26. Nugent's Pocket Dictionary, Fr. Eng. 16ˢ.
27. Dictionnaire de poche par Catineau, 12°.
28. Pronouncing Dictionary by Tardy, 12°.
29. Les Principes de la lange Française de Girard, 2 v 12°.
30. Synonimes de Diderot, Dalambert, et Jaucourt, 12°.
31. Synonimes Français de Girard, 2 v 12°.
150. Linguarum veterum Septentrionalium Thesaurus Hickesii, 2 v fol.
117. Wotlon's view of Hickes's Thesaurus, 4°.
32. Grammatica Lapponica Ganandri, 12°.
118. Lexicon Lapponicum Joh. Ihre, cum Gram. Lapponica Lindahl, 4°.
119. Sacrorum Evangeliorum versio Gothica, ab Edw. Lye, 4°.
120. Ulphilæ versio Gothica epist. Pauli ad Romanos, à Francisco Knilel, 4°.
121. Johannis ab Ihre Scripta Versionem Ulphilanum illustrantia, a Busching, 4°.
122. Grammatica Anglo-Saxonica et Moeso-Gothica, Heckesii, et Islandica Jonæ, 4°.
83. Grammatica Anglo-Saxonica ex Hickesiano Thesauro excerpta, 8°.
84. Elstob's Saxon Grammar, p 4°.
151. Lye's Dictionarium Saxonico et Gothico-Latinum, ab Owen Manning, 2 tom in 1. fol.
85. Benson's Saxon Vocabulary, 8°.
123. Evangeliorum Versiones Gothica et Anglo-Saxonica a Junio et Mareschello, et Gothicum Glossarium Junii, 2 v in 1, 4°.
86. An English-Saxon Homily, on the birth day of Sᵗ Gregory, Anglo-Sax. and Eng. by Mʳˢ Elstob, 8°.
152. Bedæ historia Ecclesiastica paraphrasi Saxonica Alfredi, fol
153. Chronologia Anglo-Saxonica a Wheeloc, fol.
124. Gibson's Saxon Chronicle, 4°.
154. Archainomia Lambardi a Wheeloc, fol.
87. Boethius, Anglo Saxonice ab Alfredo rege, 8°, Oxon.
88. Orosius, Saxon by King Alfred, and Eng. by Barrington, 8°.
89. Horne Tooke's Epea Pteroenta, or Diversions of Purley, 2 v 8°.
90. Wallisii Grammatica Linguæ Anglicanæ, 8°.
33. Lowthes Eng. Grammar, 12°
34. The British Grammar, 12°.
35. Lindley Murray's Eng. Grammar, 12°
91. Maittaire's Eng. Grammar, 8°.

130

36. English Grammar, 12°.
37. Burn's Grammar, 12°.
38. Sheridan's Eng. Grammar, 12°.
92. Waldo's Rudiments of Eng. Grammar, 8°.
39. Wilson's Philological Entertainments, 16ˢ.
93. Pointer's Academical Miscellany, 8°.
155. Etymologicon linguæ Anglicanæ Skinneri, fol.
94. Grose's Provincial Glossary, 8°.
125. Johnson's Eng. Dictionary, 2 v 4°.
40. Lexiphanes, 12°.
41. Johnson's Spelling Dictionary, 12°.
95. Walker's Critical Pronouncing Dictionary of the Eng. 8°.
96. Webster's Dictionary, 12°.
42. The Mariner's Dictionary, Duane, 12°.
126. Croft on the Eng. and German Languages, 4°.
97. Bachman's German Grammar, 8°.
43. Grammatica Todesca de Chirchmair, 12°.
127. Sewel's Dutch and Eng. Dictionary, 2 v in 1 4°.
98. Gaelick and Eng. Vocabulary, 8°.
99. The New Testament Gaelick 8° (Manks) Whitehaven 1775.
44. The New Testament, Gaidhlig, with rules for reading it, 12° Edinburgh, 1767.
45. Mac Donald's Gaelic songs and poems, with a Glossary, 12°.
46. Jones's Welsh and Eng. Dictionary, 12°.
47. The Bible in Irish, 12°.
48. Grammaire Caraïbe de Raymond, 12°.
49. Dictionnaire Caraïbe de Raymond, 2 v 12°.
50. Delaware-Indian Spelling book, by Zeisberger, 12°.
100. Claesse's Mohawk Liturgy, p 4°.

Chapter 44.

Polygraphical.

 5. Encyclopédie de Diderot et D'Alembert, 39 v 8°. Lausanne
30. Encyclopédie Méthodique de Pancoucke, 136 1/2 v. 4° Paris.
36. Chambers's Dictionary of Arts and Sciences, 2 v fol.
 6. Dictionary of Arts and Sciences, Oven, 4 v 8°.
31. American Encyclopædia, 18 v. 4°.
 7. Aristotelis Opera, Gr. Lat. 8 v. 8° Læmarii 1597
32. Ciceronis Opera, Oliveti, 9 v 4°.
 1. Ciceronis Opera, Foulis, 2 v 16.
33. Aulus Gellius, Gronovii, 4°.
 8. Alexandri ab Alexandro, geniales dies, 2 v. 8°.
 9. Macrobii Saturnalia, 8°.
10. Cassiodori opera, 8o
11. Collectanea Græca, Dalzell, 8°.
12. Collectanea Græca Minora, Dalzell, 8°.
37. Bacon's works, 4 v fol.
38. Bacon's Advancement of learning, Eng. fol.
39. Locke's works, 3 v fol.
    Locke, a collection of his pieces (in Op.)
13. Locke's familiar letters, 8° Lond. 1737.
    Locke's posthumous works, (in op.)
34. Milton's prose Works, 2 v 4°.
40. King James's Works, fol.
41. Selden's works, 6 v fol.
42. Gassendi Opera, 6 v fol.
14. Franklin's Works, 4 v 8° Duane 1809 (1st v. wanting)
15. Œuvres de Voltaire, 58 v. 8°. 1775 and 1785.
16. Œuvres de Maupertuis, 4 v 8°.
 2. Œuvres de St Real, 5 v 12°.
 3. Mélanges de Littérature, 5 v 12°.
17. Les Ecoles Normales, 3 v 8°.

18. La Création du Monde, ou Systeme d'organization primitive, par Bécourtz, 8°.

Sterne's Works, 5 v 12° (See C. 34. N°. 20.

19a. Webster's Essays, 8°.

19b. The Rainbow, 8°.

20. The Gentleman's Magazine, for 1756, 67, 68, 8° 3 v.

21. The London Magazine, from 1759 to 1769, 8° 11 v.

22. The American Monthly Magazine, 2 v 8°.

23. The Weekly Magazine, 2 v 8° 1798.

24. The National Magazine, 8° 1800.

25. Carey's American Museum, 12 v 8°.

26. Carey's Museum, for 1796, 8°.

27. The Columbian Magazine, 7 v 8°.

28. The Bee, by James Anderson, 17 v 8°.

29. The Repository, 2 v 8° 1788.

4. Dodsley's Fugitive Pieces, 2 v 12°.

35. Select Papers of the Belfast Literary Society, 4° pamphlet.

APPENDIX

Some Pages from the Printed Catalog of 1815

The following illustrations show the title page and pages from two of the forty-four chapters in the *Catalogue of the Library of the United States* (Washington: Printed for Jonathan Elliot, 1815).

After Jefferson sold his library to Congress, that body authorized the printing of a catalog of the collection. The printed catalog was based on the former President's manuscript catalog of his library but rearranged the books in an alphabetical order. Librarian of Congress George Watterston kept Jefferson's manuscript catalog after he was dismissed from his post as Librarian and it has since disappeared.

The Trist manuscript, reprinted here on the preceding pages, restores Jefferson's own order for his library. The representative chapters from the *Catalogue of the Library of the United States* reproduced below allow comparison of Jefferson's own classification of his books with the alphabetical order that Watterston devised for the printed catalog.

CATALOGUE

OF THE

LIBRARY OF THE UNITED STATES.

TO WHICH IS ANNEXED,

A COPIOUS INDEX,

ALPHABETICALLY ARRANGED.

—————

WASHINGTON.

PRINTED BY JONATHAN ELLIOT.

1815.

CHAPTER 29.

GEOGRAPHY.

GENERAL.

115	Anson's Voyage round the World, 8vo
230	Atlas Portatif de Grenet et Bonne, 4to
231	Atlas by Arrowsmith and Lewis, 4to
3	Cluverii Geographia, 24s
K	Collection of Maps, Geographical, gr. fol
L	Collection of Plans of Towns, gr. fol
111	Dionysii Orbis Descriptio, Gr. Lat. 8vo, Hill
112	Dionysii Geographia, Gr. Lat. Wells, 8vo
9	Echard's Classical Geographical Dictionary, 12mo
5	Geographie de Robbe, 2 v 12mo
6	Geographie Ancienne et Moderne de Grenet, 12mo
232	Guthrie's Geography, 2 v 4to
264	Harris's Voiages, 2 v fol
263	Heylin's Cosmography, fol
262	Moll's Geography, fol
113	Pinkerton's Geography, 2 v 8vo
1	Pomponius Mela de situ orbis, 12mo
7	Principes de Geographie, par Le Moine, 12mo
114	Scott's Universal Gazetteer, 4 v 8vo
2	Solinus Polyhistor, 12mo, Lipsiae, 1777
8	Spafford's General Geography, 12mo

260   Strabo, Gr. Lat. Casauboni, fol
  F   Tables Geographiques de Sanson, gr. fol
  4   Théatre de l'Univers de Chateaunieres, 3d vol p 8vo
261   Veteris Orbis Tabulae Geographicae, Amstelodami, Covens &
        Mortier, fol
  E   Wells's Maps of antient and present Geography, gr. fol

EUROPE.

 29   Addison's remarks on several parts of Italy, 12mo
 23   Almanac du Voiageur à Paris, de 1785, 12mo
234   Antonini iter, by Gale, 4to
123   Austin's Letters from London, 1802, 3, 8vo
 30   Burnet's travel s, 12mo
233   Busching's Geography, 6 v 4to
 17   Caractere et Mœurs des Anglois et François, 12mo
126   Coxe's Sketches of Switzerland, 8vo
 21   Curiosites de Paris, par Dulaure, 12mo
236   Dalrymple's Travels thro' Spain and Portugal, 4to
 16   Description Historique de Paris, par Piganiol de la Force, 10 v 12mo
 14   Description Universel de la France, par de Hesseln, 6 v 12mo
 10   Description de l'Islande de Horrebow, 2 v 12mo
 33   Description de Genes, 12mo
141   Essai sur la Turquie, 8vo
132   Fragmens sur Paris, par Meyer, 2 v 8vo
 27   Guide pour le Voiage d'Italie en poste, 12mo
134   Introduccion a la historia natural, y a la geografia fisica de Espana por
        Bowles, p 4to
 13   Itineraire de Dutens, 12mo
119   Keysler's Travels, 4 v 8vo
  G   Koop's 10 maps of the Rhine, the Maes, and the Sheldt, gr. format, fol
 36   Lady Montague's Letters, 12mo
129   Letters on the North, 2d vol, 8vo

125 Le Guide d'Amsterdam, 8vo

15 Le Voyageur à Paris, 12mo

19 L'Espion Chinois, 6 v 12mo

20 L'Espion Anglois, 10 v 12mo

131 L'Espion du Boulevard du Temple, 8vo

21 Les Entretiens de l'Autre Monde, 2 v 12mo

118 Marshall's Travels, 3 v 8vo

22 Memoires Secrets d'un Observateur en France, tome 22me. au 30me.
12mo 9 v

140 Memoires du Baron de Tott sur les Turcs et les Tartares, 2 v 8vo

237 Memoire Idraulo-Storiche sopra la Val. di Chiana, dal Fossombroni 4to

32 Nouva Guida di Milano, 12mo

265 Pausaniae Graeciae descriptio, Gr. Lat. Xylandri, fol Francof, 1583

116 Phipp's Voiage in (1773) towards the North Pole, 8vo

239 Randolph's account of the Morea and Archipelago in 1687, 4to

266 Sandy's travels into Italy, Greece, Turkey, the Holy Land and Egypt, fol

117 Specimen Islandiae historicum et chorographicum, per Arngrim Jonam,
p 4to, Amsterdam, 1643

235 State [Geographical] of Great Britain, 4to

18 Tableau de Paris, de Mercier, 6 v 12mo

137 The description of Greece, by Pausanias, Eng. by Taylor, 3 v 8vo

11 The Ambulator, 12mo

12 Trusler's London Adviser, 12mo

133 Ville de Nismes, 8vo

130 Vie Privée des François, par le Grand d'Aussy, 3 v 8vo

121 Voyage en Angleterre, par Faujas, 2 v 8vo

122 Voyage en Angleterre, par Pictet, 8vo

35 Voiages de Spon et Wheeler, 2 v 16s

138 Voiage literaire de la Grece, par Guys, 4 v 8vo

139 Voiage en Grece et en Turquie, par Sonnini, 2 v 8vo

28 Voiage d'Italie de Misson, 12mo

31 Voiage en Italie de M. de la Lande, 9 v 12mo

26 Voiage d'un Ametuer des Arts, 4 v 12mo

34 Voyage de Terracine a Naples, par Bayard, 12mo

238 Viaggio in Dalmazia dell' Abate Fortis, 3 v 4to

136 Voiage en Portugal, par Link, 2 v 8vo

135	Voyage en Espagne de Bourgoyne, 3 v 8vo
25	Voiage de Figaro en Espagne, 16s
127	Voyage en Suisse, par Mayer, 2 v 8vo
128	Voyage dans le Jura, par Lequinio, 2 v 8vo
129	Voyage dans les Alpes de Saussure, 4v 8vo
124	Watson's Tour in Holland, 8vo

ASIA.

153	Capper on the passage to India thro' Egypt, 8vo
144	Compendio de las historias de la India Oriental, por de la Puente, p 4to
152	Cooke's last [3d] Voyage, 4 v 8vo [published by Government]
150	Cook's last [3d] Voyage, 1776—9, anonymous, 8vo
143	Descouvertes des divers Savans voiageurs en Russie et en Perse, 4 v 8vo
242	Description de la Chine, par Grosier, 4to
148	Eden's New Holland and Botany Bay, 8vo
151	Ellis's Narrative of Cook's [3d] Voyage, 2 v 8vo
149	Hawkesworth's account of Byron's, Wallace's, Carteret's, and Cooke's
	[2d] Voiages, 4 v 8vo
39	Le Compte, Memoires sur la Chine, 2 v in 1, 12mo
42	Ledyard's Journal of Cooke's last [3d] Voyage, 12mo, Hartford, 1783
146	Macintosh's Travels, 2 v 8vo
243	Mortimer's Voyage to the Asiatic Islands and Canton, G. 4to, Lond. 1790
41	Poyvre sur les Moeurs et les Arts de l'Afrique, l'Asia, et l'Amerique, 12mo
241	Tableau Topographique et Politique de la Siberie, de la Chine, de l'Asie,
	et de l'Amerique, par Cordier de Launay, 4to
37	Voiages de Hasselquist dans Levant, 12mo
142	Voiage de la Troade, par le Chevalier, avec Atlas, 4 v 8vo
38	Voiages et descouvertes des Russes, par Muller, 2 v in 1, 12mo
240	Voiages d' Olearius et de Mandelslo, trad. par Wicquefort, 2 v 4to
267	Voiages de Chardin en Perse et aux Indes Orientales, fol
145	Voiage de le Gentil dans les Mers de l'Inde, 5 v 8vo
40	Voiage de Schouten aux Indes Orientales, 2 v 12mo
147	Woodard's Narrative of the Malays, 8vo
244	Wilson's account of the Pelew Islands, by Keate, 4to

AFRICA.

157 Bruce's Travels, 6 v 8vo
45 Description du Cap de Bonne Esperance, par Kolbe, 3 v 12mo
43 Description de l'Egypte, par Maillet, 2 v 12mo
47 Histoire de l'Afrique Françoise, par l'Abbe Demanet, 2 v 12mo
155 Lettres sur l'Egypte, par Savary, 3 v 8vo
46 Relation de l'Afrique, par de la Croix, 4 v 12mo
156 Sparmann's Voyage to the Cape of Good Hope, from 1772, to 1776, 2 v 8vo
268 Shaw's Travels, fol
154 Voyage en Syrie et en Egypte, par Volney, 2 v 8vo
245 Voyage de Denon dans la basse et la haute Egypte, 2 v 4to Lond. 1802
44 Voiage de Guinee, par Bosman, 12mo
48 Voiage de Dubois, aux isles Dauphine, de Bourbon, &c. 12mo
49 Voiage de Madagascar, 12mo

AMERICA.

224 A Collection of Voyages to the Southern Hemisphere, Magellanica, Polynesia, Australasia, &c. 2 v 8vo London, 1788
249 Adair's History of the American Indians, 4to
70 Almanac Americain, de 1784, 12mo
257 Alonzo d'Ovaglie, Historica Relacione del Regno di Cile, 4to Roma, 1646
181 American Farmer, by St. John de Crevecoeur, 8vo
208 Antonio de Leon, Tratado de Encomiendas, &c. para las Indias y Biblioteca Orient. y Occid. p 4to Madrid, 1629, 30
J Atlas Ameriquain de Rouge, gr. fol
192 Bartram's Travels thro' the Carolinas, Georgia and Florida, 8vo
202 Bartolomeo de las Casas del imperio soberano sobre las Indias, p 4to, 1552
203 Bartolomeo de las Casas Istoria della destruzzionne dell' Indie Occidentali. Span. Ital. p 4to Venezia, 1626

16

165   Barton's new views of the origin of the tribes of America, 8vo

M   Birch's Views of Philadelphia, gr. fol

201   Brackenridge's Views of Louisiana, 8vo

130   Burnaby's Travels thro' the Middle Settlements of North America,
        8vo, in 1759, 60

65   Carver's Travels, 12mo

214   Chappe d'Auteroche's voyage to California, Mexico, and Newfound-
        land, 8vo

174   Chastellux Voyages in America, 2 v 8vo

290   Commentarios reales de los Incas del Peru, por el Inca Garcilasso de la
        Vega, 2 v fol

223   Compendio della Storia del Chile, Bologna, 1776, 8vo [dal Molina?]

94   Conquete de la Mexique, par de Solis, 2 v 12mo

270   Collection des Voiages aux Indes Occidentales, par de Bry, XI parts in
        3 v fol Frankfort

185   Colles's roads of the United States, p 4to

191   Coxe's Account of Carolina, 8vo

182   Cultivateur Americain, par St. Jean de Crevecoeur, 2 v 8vo

183   Cultivateur Americain, par St. Jean de Crevecoeur, 3 v 8vo

50   Description des Cotes de l'Amerique, par Dassie, 12mo

220   Description de Surinam, par Fermin, 2 v in 1 8vo

105   Description des Terres Magellaniques, 16s

259   Description de St. Domingue, par Moreau de St. Mery, 2 v 4to

201   Diego Fernandez, Historia del Peru, Seville, 1571
        Augustin de Carate, Historia del Descubrimiento y Con-   } fol
        quista del Peru, Seville, 1571

79   Description de la Louisiane, par Hennepin, 12mo

282   Description des Indes Occidentales, par Herrera, avec la Navigation de la
        Maire, fol

271   Delle navigazione e viaggi raccolte, dal Ramusio, 3 v fol

280   De Veitia Linage, Norte de la Contratacion de las Indias Occidentales,
        fol Seville, 1672

76   Decouvertes de M. de la Sale, par Tonti, 12mo

229   Edwards's history of the British West Indies, 5 vols. 8vo

219   El Orinoco Illustrado, por Gumilla, 2 v p 4to

161   Elogio d'Amerigo Vespucci, dal Canovai, 8vo

253 Ellicot's Journal of the boundary of Florida, 4to

278 Fernando Pizarro y Orellana, Varones Illustres, del Nuevo Mundo, fol Madrid, 1639

84 Gass's Journals of Lewis and Clarke's journey of discovery to the Pacific, 12mo

209 General history of the Continent and Islands of America, by Herrera, 6 v 8vo

289 Gio. Gioseppe di S. Teresa, Istoria delle guerre del Brazile, tra il Portogallo e la Olanda, fol Roma, 1698

225 Hakluyt's history of the West Indies, p 4to

269 Hakluyt's Voiages, fol 1st edition

88 Historia del Mondo Nuovo del Benzoni, Ven. 1572
Bart. de las Casas, tyran. des Espagnols es Ind. Occid. Anv. 1579 } 12mo

205 Historia natural y moral de las Indias, por Joseph de Acosta, p 4to Sevilla, 1590

206 Historia natural y moral de las Indias, por Joseph de Acosta, p 4to Madrid, 1608

281 Historia general de las islas y tierra firma del mar Oceano di Herrara, 5 v fol

281 Historia de la Conquista de la Nueva Espana, por Bernal Diaz del Castillo, fol Madrid, 1632

285 Historia de Nueva Espana, por Hernan Cortes, fol

93 Historia de Mexico, con el Discubrimiento de la Nueva Espana, por Lopez di Gomara, 12mo Anvers, 1554

251 Historia de la Conquista de Mexico, por de Solis, 2 v 4to

101 Historia del Peru da Pietro Cieza di Leone, Ven. 1560
Historia del India, Ven. 1566
Conquista di Messico da Lopez di Gomara, Ven. 1565 } 5 v 12mo
La Conquista de Messico y de la Nueva Espana, por Lopez di Gomara, Anvers, 1554

57 Histoire des Flibustiers, par Oexmelin, 4 v 12mo

87 Histoire General des Indes Occidentales, traduite par Fumée, p 8vo Paris, 1565, 1584

95 Histoire de l'Oronoque, par Gumilla, traduite par Eidous, 3 v 12mo

221 Histoire Naturel de Surinam, par Fermin, 8vo

100 Histoire de Paraguay de Charlevoix, 6 v 12mo

142

  98 Histoire d'une Voiage faite en Brazil, par Jean de Lery, 12mo
 108 Histoire Naturel des Antilles, par de Rochefort, 2 v 12mo
 109 Histoire des Antilles Angloises, 12mo
 110 Histoire de la Jamaique, trad. de Anglois, 12mo
 258 Histoire des Navigations aux Terres Australes, 2 v 4to
  60 Histoire de la Nouvelle France, par Lescarbot, 12mo
  61 Histoire de la Nouvelle France, par de Charlevoix, 6 v 12mo
  63 Histoire de l'Amerique Septentrionale, par de la Potherie, 4 v 12mo
  66 Histoire Geographique de la Nouvelle Ecosse, 12mo
  72 Histoire de la Pennsylvanie prise sur Kalm, et Mittelburger, 12mo
 193 Histoire de Kentucky de Filson, 8vo
 250 History of the British Dominions in North America, 4to
 272 Hist. Universelle des Indes Occid. par Corneille Wytflict, et des Indes
       Orient. par Anthoine Magin, 2 v fol
 217 Houston's Memoirs, 8vo
 212 Humboldt's Political Essay on New Spain, Eng. 2 v 8vo
   I Jeffery's American Atlas, fol gr.
 273 Jeffery's Natural and Civil History of the French Dominions in
       America, fol
 277 Joannes de Salorzano Pereira de Indiarum jure, fol Madrid, 162 9
 166 Jones's Journal to the Indian Nations, 8vo
  77 Journal du dernier voyage de M. de la Sale, par Joutel, 12mo
  82 Journal d'un Voiage à la Louisiane en 1720, 12mo
 187 Kalm's Travels into North America, by Forster, 2 v 8vo
 196 La Sale's last voyage to the gulf of Mexico, by Joutel, 8vo
 283 La Monarquia Indiana, por de Torquemada, 3 v fol
 248 Lafitau, Moeurs des Sauvages Americains, 2 v 4to Paris 1724
 275 La Florida por de la Vega, et por de Cardenas y Caro, 2 v fol [duplicate
       of the preceding]
  86 La decouverte des Indes Occidentales, par Balthasar de las Casas, 12mo
  83 Le Page du Pratz, history of Louisiana, 2 v 12mo
 279 Le Nouveau Monde de Du Laet, fol 1640
  53 Le Voiageur François, par de la Porte, vol 6—14, 12mo 9 v
  68 Le Pour et le Contre des Etats Unis, par Bridel, 12mo
  52 Le Lettere Americane del Conte Carli, 3 v 12mo

143

102 Levini Apollonii Gandobrugani de **Peruviae** Inventione et rebus Gestis. Antwerp, 1567, p 8vo

171 **Lewis and Clark's** Expedition to the Pacific Ocean, 2 v 8vo

167 **Loskeil's Mission** among the Indians of America, 8vo

274 { **La Florida** por el Inca Garcilasso de la Vega, fol Madrid, 1723 \ Historia General de la Florida, por de Cardenas y Caro, 2 vols. fol Madrid, 1723

74 **Maese's** Picture of Philadelphia, 12mo

170 **Mackenzie's** voyages across North America to the Pacific Ocean, 2 v 8vo

178 **Mellish's** travels in the United States of America, 2 v 8vo

207 **Milicia** y descripcion de las Indias, por Bernardo de Vargas Machuca, p 4to Madrid, 1599

78 **Memoires** sur la Louisiane, par Dumont, 2 v 12mo

216 **Memoires** sur l'Amerique, par Don Ulloa, traduites par Villebrun, 2 v 8vo

99 **Meridien** de Demarcation entre l'Espagne et le Portugal en Amerique, par Ulloa, 12mo

158 **Morse's** American Geography, 8vo

159 **Morse's** American Gazetteer, 8vo

204 **Naufragios** y comentarios de Alvar Nunez en dos jornadas a las Indias, p 4to, Valladol. 1555

190 **Notes** on Virginia, Original Edition, 8vo

215 **Noticias** Americanas de Don Antonio de Ulloa, 8vo

56 **Nouvelle** relation de la Gaspesie, par Chrestien le Clerc, 12mo 1675—81

80 **Nouvelle** Decouverte d'un tres grand Pais dans l'Amerique, par Henepin, 1st and 3d vol. 12mo

81 **Nouveau** Voiage d'un pays plus grand que l'Europe, par Hennepin, 12mo

90 **Novae** novi orbis historiae ex Italicis Benzoni latine reddita Urbani Calvetonis industrià, cui ab eodem adjuncta est Gallorum in Floridam Expeditio, p 8vo

213 **Notitia** de la California, por Miguel Venegas, 3 v p 4to [a copy presented to Father Charlevoix]

288 **Observaciones** Astronomicas y Physicas, por Juan y Ulloa, fol

73 **Ogden's** Excursion to Bethlehem, 12mo

67 **Ogden's** tour thro' Canada, 12mo

226 **Oldmixon's** history of the British Islands in America, 8vo

144

H   Ortelii Theatrum Orbis, gr. fol

158   Pamphlets on Indians, Topographical, &c. 8vo

276   Pedro Simon de Cuença Noticias de las Conquistas en las Ind. Occid.
           fol Cuença, 1626

83   Petrus Martyr Anglerius de orbe novo, edente Richard Hakluyt, p 8vo
           Paris, 1587

199   Pike's Expeditions to the sources of the Mississippi, and thro' the western
           parts of Louisiana, 8vo

169   Present state of Nova Scotia, 8vo, 1786

247   Purchas's Pilgrimage, p fol

64   Relation Ecclesiastique de la Nouvelle France, 1643, 4, par Vimont 12mo

54   Relation de divers voiages en Afrique et Amerique, par de Grande
           Pierre 12mo

51   Recherches sur les Americains, par Paw, 3 v 12mo

222   Restauracion de la Ciudad del Salvador en Brazil, por Tamaio de
           Vargas, p 4to Madrid, 1628

184   Roll of Officers in 1802, 8vo

172   Rogers's Account of North America, 8vo

85   Romans's history of Florida, 12mo

75   Scott's Geography of Maryland and Virginia, 12mo

69   Scott's United States Gazetteer, 12mo

197   Second Voiage à la Louisiane, par Baudry, 2 v 8vo

200   Stoddart's Sketches of Louisiana, 8vo

252   Stork's description of East Florida, and Bartram's Journal, 4to

255   Storia del Messico dell' Abate Clavigero, 4 v 4to

186   Spafford's Gazetteer of the State of New York, 8vo 1813

160   Tableau des Etats Unis, par Pictet, 8vo

228   The Navigation of St. Domingo, Puysegur, 8vo

N   The English Pilot, 4th Book, gr. fol

210   The Spanish Empire in America, 8vo

96   The history of Miranda's attempt to effect a Revolution in South America,
           by an Officer, 12mo

71   The New York Guide, 12mo

195   Tracts Geographical, Elliot, Tatham, Sharp, Constable, 8vo

188   Tracts on Virginia, and New England, by Bullock, Thomas Morton,
           Roberts, Coke and others, p 4to 1609—71

179 Tracts on America, to wit, Palairet's Eng. and Fr. possessions— Br. and French Colonies—Stork's E. Florida—Barton Nat. Hist.—Examen de Chastellux — Remarks on Chastellux — Federal Lands, Ohio Company 8vo

257 Viage a la America Meridional, por Jorge Juan y Antonio de Ulloa, 4 v fol

189 Virginia by E. W. p 4to

246 Vita e lettere di Amerigo Vespucci, 4to dal Bandini

97 Voiages de Des Marchais en Guinée et Cayenne, par Labat, 4 v 12mo

91 Voiages de Correal, viz. la Floride, Antilles, Mexique, N. Grenade, Guyane, Brezil, Peru, Philippines, Terres Australes, 1666—1697, 2 v 12mo

59 Voiages dans l'Amerique Septentrionale, par de Lahontan, 2 v 12mo

55 Voiages de Bossu aux Indes Occidentales, 12mo

62 Voiage parmi les Sauvages de l'Amerique Septentrionale, par le Beau, 3 v 12mo

O 286 Voiage de Humboldt, 3me partie Essai sur la Nouvelle Espagne, et 4me partie, Astronomie et Magnetisme, gr. fol

251 Voiage de la Louisiane en 1720, par le Pere Laval, 4to

58 Voiage au pays des Hurons, par Sagard, 2 v in 1, 12mo

211 Voiage de la Condamine dans l'Amerique Meridionale, 2 v 8vo

114 Voiage de Marseille a Lima, par Durret, 12mo

256 Voiage aux Cotes du Chily et du Perou en 1712, 3, 4, par Frezier, 2 v 4to

106 Voiage autour du Monde et aux Terres Australes de Dampier, et le Voyage de Wafer, 4 v 12mo

163 Voyages to North America, by Lahontan, 2 v 8vo

173 Voyages de Chastellux en Amerique, 2 v 8vo

162 Voyages de Pages autour du Monde et vers les Deux Poles, 3 v in 2 8vo

92 Voyages de Thomas Gage dans la Nouvelle Espagne, 2 v 12mo

177 Voyage de Liancour dans les Etats Unis, 8 v 8vo

194 Voyage à l'Ouest des Monts Alleghaneys, par F. A. Michaux, 8vo

175 Voyage de Brissot de Warville dans les Etats Unis, 3 v 8vo

164 Voyage de la Nouvelle France, par le Sieur de Champlain, p 4to

218 Voyage aux isles de Trinidad, de Tabago, de la Marugerite, et dans la Venezuela, par la Vaysse, 2 v 8vo 1813

146

227　Voyage d'un Suisse dans differentes Colonies de l'Amerique, 8vo
107　Voyage de Labat aux isles de l'Amerique, 6 v 12mo
176　Volney, Tableau du climat et du sol des Etats Unis d'Amerique, 2 v
　　　　in 1, 8vo
198　Vue de la Louisiane et Floride Occidentale, par Duvallon, 8vo
103　Zarate, Histoire de la Decouverte et de la Conquete de Perou, 2 v 12mo

CHAPTER 30.

FINE ARTS.

ARCHITECTURE.

18 Antichita di Roma del Scamozzi, fol

5 Architettura del Alberti, p 4to

15 Architecture de Le Clerc, 4to

6 Bibliotheque d'Architecture de Jombert, partie 4me. Parallele de l'Architecture antique et moderne, par Errard et Chambray, et 2de partie Architecture de Palladio, 2 v 8vo

T Castell's Villas of the Antients, gr. fol

Z Chambers's Chinese Designs, gr. fol

23 Chippendale's Cabinet Maker's Designs, fol

17 Dictionnaire d'Architecture, civile, militaire, et navale, par De Virloys, 3 v in 2 4to

11 Discours sur les Monumens Publics, par Kersaint, 4to
    [De la Faye sur la chaux des Romains, 8vo] ante C. 15, 69

19 Edifices anciennes de Rome, par Desgodetz. fol, Paris 1779

16 Elementi di Architettura del Padre Sanvitali
    Elementi di Architettura del Preti
    Nuove richerche sull' Equilibrio delle volte del Abate Mascheroni   } 4to
    Etienne d'un Ciment impenetrable à l'Eau

29 Gibb's Rules for Drawing in Architecture, fol

W Gibb's Designs in Architecture, gr. fol

3 Halfpenny's practical Architecture, 12mo

X Inigo Jones's and Ld. Burlington's Designs, by Kent, gr. fol
  17

25	Il settimo l'bro d'Architettura del Serglio, Ital. Lat. ⎫
	Regola delle cinque Ordine d'Architettura del Vignola ⎬ fol
	Les cinq Ordres d'Architecture de Scamozzi, par Daviler ⎭
B B	Kirby's Perspective of Architecture, on Brook Taylor's Principles, 2 v g fol
30	Langley's practical Geometry, fol
24	L'Architecture de Vitruve de Perrault, fol
29	Lubersac sur les Monumens publiques, fol
12	Meinert's Schone land baukunst, or Ideas of Buildings, 4to, Leipzig 1798
V	Mitchell's Perspectives of Buildings in England and Scotland, and his Gothic Architecture, Fr. Eng. gr. fol
U	Monumens de Louis XV, par Patte, gr. fol
S	Monumens de Nismes de Clerissault, gr. fol
14	Morris's Select Architecture and Designs, 4to
21	Plans des Maisons de Paris, par Krafft et Ransonette, fol
22	Plans d'Architecture, par Becker, fol
26	Palladio, by Leoni, with Inigo Jones's notes, fol
27	Palladio, by Leoni, Ital. Fr. and Eng. 2 v fol
28	Palladio, les 4 livres d'Architecture, par de Chambray ⎫
	Perrault's five orders of Architecture, by James ⎬ fol
	De Lorme, Invention pour batir les Couvertures courbes ⎭
13	Portefeuille de Artistes, ou Desseins et Plans de Chateaux, Maisons, &c. 4to Leipsic, 1800
1	Ritratto di Roma Antiqua 12mo
2	Ritratto di Roma Moderna 12mo
8	Roma Illustrata, Donati, 4to
P	Ruins of Balbec, by Wood and Dawkins, gr. fol
Q	Ruins of Athens, by Le Roy, fol
R	Ruins of Athens, by Stuart and Revett, gr. fol
4	Scamozzi's Architecture, by Leyburn, p 4to
Y	Smeaton's Narrative of Eddystone Lighthouse, gr. fol
7	The Builder's Dictionary, 2 v 8vo
9	Vestigia é rarita di Roma del Ficorone, 4to
10	Varie vedute di Roma antica e moderna, del Piranesi, fol